SIM

CHANGES

Your 100 ways to a happier, healthier life

PHILLIP DAY

C Credence Publications

Simple Changes

First published in 2006
by Credence Publications

ISBN 1-904015-20-4

Manufactured in Great Britain and Australia by
Credence Publications
PO Box 3
TONBRIDGE
Kent TN12 9ZY UK
www.credence.org

1st ed.

Table of Contents

Introduction

Dear Reader

Thank you for taking the time to read this book!

What a subject. What can we do, starting right now, to change things for a happier, healthier life? What do the experts recommend? Why should we care?

I am a health researcher, author and international speaker who, for the past twenty years, has been fascinated by attitudes to sickness, health and longevity. In fact, the brief of my company, Credence, runs quite a bit wider than just health issues. We report on agendas that are harmful to the public, and our mission now is based in many countries around the world.

The first thing I have to do is to convince you you're worth working on, and me too (this book has been superb therapy). Of course, no-one taught us Life Management at school, those skills everyone needs to survive and thrive in the 21st Century, and what a pity. You'd think the most common-sense thing in the world would be to improve education, give kids the tools they'll need to overcome, and help society steer itself down the middle path to glory. Not a bit of it.

As time goes by, the opposite seems to be occurring, and thanks for your letters and e-mails, by the way, for which I am grateful. They tell me it's business as usual on Planet Earth. More war in the Middle East. The polar icecaps are melting along with the bears. Sickness and obesity abound. Students in Britain are told they can choose their own values system or none at all (37%

in certain exams will earn you an 'A'). The St George's Cross can be banned from fluttering in your back garden for fear of inciting race-hatred.

Dozing in front of *The 100 Most Embarrassing TV Moments* last year on Channel 4, my head snapped up like it does with an epiphany, and I was given to thinking, *why not do a 100 list people can really get their teeth stuck into?* Maybe like:

Don't die badly
The sky rarely falls in
Don't be too clean (??)
START @!!&$$ COMPLAINING?

Well, it took a while, but here we go: *Simple Changes, Your 100 Ways to a Happier, Healthier Life.* Now, don't go thinking the following are chiselled into tablets of stone. And don't get overly niggled if I get on my high horse on occasion about issues that prickle my porcupine. As founder of the Campaign for Truth in Medicine, that's what I'm paid to do. To pause and consider the part each of us can play in maintaining the status quo (now in their sixties, by the way, and looking quite well on it). We could all use a little improvement. To be fair-minded and reasonable when things don't go our way. To cry 'Foul!' because if we don't, nobody else will. To care enough. To love more. To understand in tragic times that having a heart to begin with is a downright prerequisite for breaking it.

I am, of course, describing the human condition. *Simple Changes* celebrates the start of the 21st Century not just by poking holes in it. The world is fretful, multi-faceted, and we live in an era of often astonishing change and retrograde progress. In politics, the pendulum swings one way, the pendulum swings another. Fashionable causes are dangerous when their extremes enslave. People need structure, not prisons. I believe the 21st Century will stumble across the middle course eventually and we'll see a people's victory - a victory for common-sense - wherein inspiration, justice and responsibility are fetched out of the dustbin and made great again, when we've finally tired of experiencing yet another society we'd rather not live in.

'You live and learn,' Douglas Adams grumbled. *'Well, at any rate, you live.'*

Charge!

Phillip

How to Use this Book

Please Read This First ☺

Simple Changes is not designed to replace qualified medical advice. Patients suffering ill-health are, of course, advised to consult a physician. This book *does* encourage you to be discriminatory in what you do with the advice you receive, and to take control of your healthcare decisions. Ultimately it is up to you to decide on the course of action most appropriate. And, as usual, the *caveat* is well repeated that doctors and other professionals are our servants not masters, an arrangement all too easily forgotten.

This book should not be construed as diagnostic or giving treatment advice for any individual's particular condition. Information contained in *Simple Changes* is for educational purposes only. Many of the following sections deal with lifestyle problems. For more information concerning physical or 'mental' conditions, please refer to *The ABC's of Disease* and Credence's other health titles. A summary of these is given under **Other Disorders** at the end of this book.

Right enough of that. Let's get busy with *this!*

~ 100 ~
You're Never Too Old to Change

'Let others lead small lives, but not you. Let others argue over small things, but not you. Let others cry over small hurts, but not you. Let others leave their future in someone else's hands, but not you.' – **Jim Rohn**

World-renowned behavioural expert Anthony Robbins declares *'Your past does not equal your future'*, and he's right. Up until our last moment on Earth, each of us is a work in motion with skills, needs, desires and goals. The past can only enslave us if we allow it to. Just because yesterday was unfortunate does not mean today has to be the same. Every day we make choices. If we make different ones we get different results. Making the most of life, behavioural gurus agree, is about making better choices and knowing why we're making them. A celebration of experience, then, even enlightenment.

So there are some things about you you don't like, areas you feel uncomfortable. How badly do you want to fix them? How badly depends on how much discomfort the problem causes you. Discomfort prompts action. *Extreme* discomfort prompts *immediate* action. Robbins calls this 'gaining leverage', the point of critical mass. You're fed up with smoking and you're going to do something about it. Not next year. Not next week. *Now.*

Acute discomfort in finance, employment and ill-health should bring us to the point where we gain leverage and action is inevitable. We can even increase our discomfort to push ourselves over the threshold into action. All one hundred points in this book will provoke some sort of response from you, from indifference to strong emotion. Strong responses may indicate areas you wish to deal with.

- Are there things about you, you want to change?
- How badly do you want to change them?
- Badly enough to do something about it?
- *'Your past does not equal your future!'*

~ 99 ~
Time is Your Most Precious Resource

'Time wasted only when sprinkling perfume on goat farm.' - **Charlie Chan**

You can loser a tenner and it hurts, but you'll always make another.

You'll never get another 15th June 2006 again.

Time is absolutely your most precious resource.

You can set yourself up for more time by looking after yourself better, giving up lifestyle traits that rob you of time, and doing all the right things. Sounds good but how do you do it? What if you've tried but just cannot change?

Though many of the *Simple Changes* icons deal with maximising each day's potential, a few give you the tools to bring this about by *changing your behaviour*. Reference the following sections:

Set Goals
Guard Input
Work at Self-Improvement
Own a Good Conscience
Deal With Addictions
Obtain Control Over Your Sense of Certainty
Dare to Dream
Develop a Belief System

These will help you to:

- Avoid micromanaging each day
- Greatly reduce worry
- Change the way you view the world around you
- Agree with yourself in advance how the day will go
- Prioritise important tasks effortlessly
- Pack more quality into the week
- Manage the pace of your life and dissipate stress
- Ensure a healthy balance between work and play
- Enjoy more
- Accomplish more
- Experience the satisfaction of a day well lived

Appreciating that time is your most precious resource is not about trying to cheat the Reaper (you won't), it's accepting that another day has arrived with yet another chance to work on your masterpiece. You will control the speed of delivery and content. You'll be the architect of your own destiny. What will you do today? What skills do you possess? What do you wish to accomplish by bedtime tonight?

~ 98 ~
Set Goals Daily

Most live their days 'on the fly' with no real planning - I did it for years. Got up, had something to eat, went to work, came home, watched TV, went to bed. These days I'm more of a fan of imagining every day as a life. Mine. It has a beginning, a middle and an end. I do the following every morning:

- I wake up (always a good idea)
- I lie in bed and contemplate the day ahead
- I ask: What do I wish to accomplish by bed-time tonight?
- How will I feel if I succeed?
- Which of these things do I personally want?
- Does the day I am planning impress the heck out of me?

Today, I will not worry about the G8 summit, a Martian invasion, suicide bombs in Baghdad, Third World hunger, an asteroid striking the Earth, or what David Beckham wore to the Met Bar last night. Today I will leave the TV off, the newspaper in the corner store, the radio silent, and clean up my input. I can be the architect of this new day which has been given to me. I intend to raise my standards and live them well.

The Possibilities Are Endless

- I will write the first page of my new book. Just one page
- I will speak to one person who thinks I've forgotten them
- I will practise what I am good at
- I will dominate my day and carefully steer it
- I will simplify, simplify, simplify
- I will guard what comes out of my mouth

- I will do no harm to myself or others
- I will eat food that nourishes me
- I will relish the freedom from negative input

Repetition in a state of emotion forms the attitude pattern. Every day I do this makes the following day easier. Six days of accomplishment means a whole week I have lived well. So much done in one week! Negative input was out, all the positives in. I ate simple, fresh, nutritious food. I drank clean water. I breathed. I did not watch *King of the Hill.*

Give Yourself a Bonus!

I *agree* to enjoy at least one overwhelming, optimistic experience (placebo) every day. Each day is planned around this event. If all else fails and the Martians invade, Samantha and I will still take Rosie for a walk in the forest. The dog's tail drums in anticipation. I know things about Labradors. They are not worried about their bank manager or a Sarin gas attack on the Bakerloo Line. It's about rabbits chased, the swim in the pond and aroma plethora.

Setting *daily* goals has great advantages:

- You agree with yourself in advance what you are going to do. This makes unwelcome chores easier
- Distractions are kept to a minimum
- You customise your day to suit you, not the other way around
- More of Oprah's quality time is packed into the day
- Longer tasks are easy when kept tightly on target
- You agree with yourself the day will have the outcome you desire

- You can 'debrief' your day back in bed again to see if it went according to plan
- You can experience success in a single day

Setting goals and debriefing takes me sixty seconds flat. I do not micro-manage, just get a clear, mental image of what I wish to accomplish by day's end. If I did it right, there's satisfaction by nightfall. If I didn't do it right, there's always tomorrow for another go.

Distractions

Impromptu events can take the best-planned days well into the hedgerow:

- The water main blew outside in the street
- You had an accident
- A phone call forced you to re-prioritise your day
- You had an unexpected visitor

If distractions force you to re-plan, simply amend the question to: *What do I wish to accomplish with the day I have left?*

UNLESS ABSOLUTELY NECESSARY, DO NOT SHELVE YOUR OVERWHELMING, OPTIMISTIC EXPERIENCE!!

- 97 -
The Sky Rarely Falls In

'The voters have spoken, the bastards.' - **Richard Nixon**

Some of us imprison ourselves daily with the fear of the unknown, of wretched things that might befall us. Perhaps there's a situation we've watched develop for some time and its direst outcome now has us jerking us awake in the wee hours, heart thumping, brow bursting forth in a cold sweat.

Few of the techniques described in *Simple Changes* work as well as the firm belief the universe is generally working for your benefit if only you can get out of the bed in the morning. Most of us own up to a sense life appears to be some sort of learning process, that there's a point to it all. (Some don't - more about them later). Clad in our four-dimensional physicality, we have little choice but to experience life. And regrettably we *do* live in a fallen world wherein dire things happen all the time - wars, accidents, financial woes, illness and death. And some of these will show up on our doorstep at some point, unbidden, unwelcome, to be our choice in determining how best we will deal with them.

I believe in taking prudent, non-obsessive steps to prepare for the worst. I believe in taking prudent, non-obsessive steps to do my best to prevent the worst. Having thus taken action, what I *won't* do is perish the death of a thousand cuts, torturing myself over what *might* happen. Worrying implies the steps I have taken will not be sufficient, therefore I worry, in spite of the fact that having taken action, matters are now beyond my ability to control them.

'What if?' That nagging voice. *'What if? What if?'*

Worrying is a survival response to hone our reactions to danger. *Chronic* worry corrupts our most precious resource - time. Chronic worry is the result of the brain's repetitive conditioning, but you'll be delighted to learn the old squashola can be educated back into conforming to a more 'damn-the-torpedoes' attitude with a few simple techniques.

Facing Your Mountains - Worry

Do not dwell on impromptu, evil imaginings. You can't stop the birds flying over your head, you can stop 'em nesting in your hair. The best way over mountains is one rock at a time. The best advice about mountains is to face them. Mountains cause worry, but not if you overcome them. *Be an overcomer.*

Things You Can Do Something About

Divide a sheet of paper vertically down the middle with a line. On the left, write down all the things that worry you which you CAN do something about. On the right, list the things that worry you, which you CANNOT do anything about.

Rank the left-hand column in descending order of bother, i.e. the most worrisome problem at the top. Do the same with the right-hand column of worries you are powerless to do anything about.

- You are now staring at your mountains
- You have an order of worries to tackle, commencing with the most worrying
- Worry caused by the problems you can do something about will diminish ONCE YOU TAKE ACTION

- Imagine each problem resolved and how you will feel
- Imagine the relief you will gain by overcoming
- Dwell on the peace of mind you will gain by overcoming
- Imagine the continued pain/anxiety of not overcoming
- List out the steps required to overcome the problem
- How badly do you want to conquer the problem?
- Now take action, focusing repeatedly on the relief you will gain at every step
- Be consistent and repetitive

Things You Cannot Do Anything About

Problems beyond your control cause unnecessary worry. There can be no action, since the problem is beyond your capacity to influence it, so why worry?

Yeah, but -

- I'm going to die one day (perhaps today)
- A super-quake *might* snap California off into the Pacific
- An asteroid *might* strike the Earth
- The sun *might* flame out, plunging the planet into darkness
- A tsunami *might* re-engulf Indonesia
- My family *might* perish in a freak accident
- I *might* become a victim of terrorists

Imagine the relief of not having to burden yourself with matters beyond your control. While you cannot fix the whole world, sometimes you *can* fix your little corner of it. Is your worry caused by junk input? You can, of course, take action on a smaller scale if you want to wimp out:

- Move out of California
- Don't take your holidays in Jakarta

- Then again, *why worry?*

Overcoming worry is about confronting the worry itself to see what the trigger process is, examining it dispassionately, then deleting the trigger in a state of positive emotion with a change in focus. In *The Little Book of Attitude*, I show you how to do this. How about some mental preparation to begin with?

- A coward dies a thousand deaths, a brave man dies but one
- I can be brave. *Why worry?*
- Terrorism fails when I fail to be terrorised. *Why worry?*
- Have I actually experienced terrorism?
- Are my worries disproportionate to the things that actually happen to me?
- Am I reacting reasonably?
- Am I living, as far as possible, a blameless life?
- Why don't I restrict input (esp. media), which fosters unnecessary worry?
- Why not give my life meaning and context to explain why I am here in the first place?
- If I live my life well, my journey's end will be expected, even welcomed

Note: Worriers perfect the art of imagining how things will turn out for the worst. Non-worriers *take prudent action* to reduce a threat, then dwell in the expectation *something good is going to happen!*

~ 96 ~

Be an Overcomer

'Most problems don't exist until a government agency is created to solve them.' – **Kirk Kirkpatrick**

Today, problem-solving skills are generally not taught in schools, resulting in a new generation of men and women facing social problems with no tools to overcome them. The trade-off is simple. For some loss of our personal freedoms, Big Government will shoulder our woes in return for an ever-increasing chunk of our income. Only it doesn't. But we keep coughing up.

It's no secret politicians are attempting to reinvent themselves by becoming guardians of the public good. Me, I'm not overflowing with confidence. Today's Britain has around 7,000 non-elected committees (quangos) directing almost every aspect of our lives under the eye of, and usually paid for by HM Government (i.e. my money). It's no secret either the Nanny-State approach has failed on many levels, for example with crime, education and health. It *has* succeeded in wasting billions, horribly raising taxes, and dissuading millions from making choices in their own self-interest, mostly in the name of saving us from ourselves.

More so than ever we need victors these days not victims. What if we re-learned the skills our forefathers employed to overcome problems that these days seem insurmountable? We'll be looking at a whole spectrum of these as we proceed. It all starts with *us*. If something about me needs changing, I need to change it. I stopped overcoming. Time for me to overcome.

- 95 -
You Are What You Eat

'MacDonalds in Tokyo is a terrible revenge for Pearl Harbor.' - **S I Hayakawa**

Every day we have a choice about what we eat. From a biochemical standpoint, however, there are no choices. Make the wrong choices consistently and Nature will sharpen her sword for us.

Every cell in our body comes from what we eat. Eat burgers for fifteen years, become a burger. The body you presently inhabit is the sum total of everything you've ever done to yourself. Don't like the body? Do something different to the body.

Dr Ted Morter Jr. has spent a lifetime analysing the effects of different foods on our internal environment and wonders why doctors are not trained in nutrition. Morter states that the body responds perfectly to every stimulus that is applied to it, each of these body responses geared towards one aim and one aim only - survival.[1]

Sometimes this response is termed 'disease' by the orthodoxy if it goes against its ideal of what 'health' should be. Morter states that the human body likes to dwell in a slight alkali (around pH 7.4). When we acidify our internal environment with certain foods or lifestyle choices, the body is forced to neutralise (buffer) this acid using a number of ingenious systems, mostly comprising alkalising minerals, like sodium, calcium, potassium,

---

[1] **Morter, M T** *An Apple a Day?* BEST Research, Inc. 1997

magnesium and iron. Urine pH is not necessarily crucial but blood pH most certainly is. Blood pH must always be between 7.35 and 7.45, Morter reports, or life ends abruptly within a matter of hours.[2]

Foods we eat leave an 'ash' in our system. Rather than the flaky stuff that gets all over the carpet when we blow on an old fire, food residues in the body can be solid or liquid, but the 'ash' they leave will be acid or alkali and, on the odd occasion, neutral. One of the main acid generators are proteins, whether derived from animal or other sources.

Osteoporosis, heart disease, cancer, arthritis, diabetes and other ailments can all be traced to the body's attempts to survive. They can also all be traced to a deficiency in the raw materials (vitamins, minerals, fats, enzymes, etc) required to get the survival job done.[3] Professor John Beard of Edinburgh University discovered cancer was a healing process that hadn't terminated upon completion of its task. The reason? Malnutrition and an acid-beleaguered immune system.[4]

External (or internal) damage done to the body will always provoke a healing response. When we detect the nature of that response, we may exclaim, "Ah, a symptom!" but as Morter declares, the body doesn't care whether you like the results of its

---

[2] Natural (physiological) acid produced through normal cell respiration is easily expelled in the breath via the lungs. Our blood pH is normally 7.35 when it is transporting this acid, in the form of carbon dioxide, to the lungs for elimination. Blood is pH 7.45 once it has been 'cleaned up', the CO_2 removed and oxygen taken on board to deliver to your heart and rest of the body.

[3] **Day, Phillip** *Health Wars*, Credence, 2003

[4] **Day, Phillip** *B17 Metabolic Therapy*, Credence, 2002

survival efforts or not. When you eat, drink, breathe, exercise, rest and think, you elicit a response from your body. So 'health' and 'disease' can be termed 'the effects of your body's responses'. Diarrhoea, vomiting, colds, flu, arthritis, rashes, osteoporosis and diabetes may not be anyone's idea of a good time, but these conditions are the result of the body's response to a stimulus. As Morter says, if you don't like the body's response, change the stimulus.

All that to say this: The experts now agree food and water are by far and away the most important factors in our health and survival (I can't believe I'm telling you this). Less well known are the consequences of our body's responses to acid and alkali. Cultures I've covered in other books live to grand old ages in fine fettle if their diet is predominantly alkaline.[5] Western nations like Britain and America, on the other hand, have a significant portion of the population crunching Rennies and Tums to smother the acid, with some unsavoury problems in the future to look forward to.

Alkali Bodies Absorb Oxygen

Nobel Prize winner Dr Otto Warburg noted alkaline systems absorb up to 20 times more oxygen than acidic systems. Diseased bodies are acidic bodies which repel oxygen and attract overgrowths of bacteria and yeast. Warburg worked with almost 50 species of animals and was able to induce cancer in animal tissue by acidifying it to drive out the oxygen. Experiments with ulcerated breast mass and other tumour material demonstrate malignant cells grow prolifically in acid, anaerobic environments, but shrivel and die in calcium- and oxygen-rich alkalis.[6]

---

5 **Day, Phillip** *Health Wars,* op. cit.

6 Ibid.

Consider a dietary change to:

Alkali residue foods: fruits, vegetables, pulses, legumes, haricots – anything grown in a kitchen garden, *80% of food intake*

Acidic residue foods: meats, dairy products, grains, processed foods, sugars, alcohol, etc, *20% of food intake*

For most people these days it's the reverse.

Acidosis

An acidic system drives out oxygen, laying the foundations for cell-death and disease. Heartburn (acid reflux), indigestion, diarrhoea, bowel problems, and mineral loss are all indicators this disease environment is coming together. In addition, most of us are chronically dehydrated because we don't drink enough water or eat high-water-content food any more. Constipation, asthma, heartburn, colitis and more problems than I've got time to shake a stick at invariably result.[7] Your cells don't go a bundle on being chronically bathed in acid either inside or outside the cell, so there's a potassium buffer response which raises the pH of the intercellular environment. Further acid will provoke the kidneys into producing more ammonia to alkalise the excreta before the acid burns holes in the delicate tissues of your kidneys, bladder and urethra.

By which time you've managed to scoot down to the doctor's waiting room to get a prescription to treat the symptoms of being stabbed in the guts with a WW1 bayonet (remember, drugs treat

---

7 Actually, I did shake a stick! See ***Day, Phillip*** *The ABC's of Disease*, Credence, 2003, for a listing of over eighty conditions and what you can do about them (www.credence.org)

'symptoms', not the underlying cause). GPs are mostly unaware of the alkali/acid struggle going on in their patients; they are certainly unaware of the nutrition and parasite causations due to no training in these areas.

Drugs given to a patient will elicit their own responses from the body (side-effects), many of which are acidic. You'll be doing yourself no favours either in the custom coffee houses, nor guzzling down all those high-sugar sodas which fool the body into believing a meal's on its way, so the body produces more acid.

Clinical urine analysis is useful to gain information on what the body is throwing away, but since we're all busy people, my simple take on the subject is this: Recognise the signs of an acidic, internal environment and begin moving it towards a harmonious alkali. Tea, coffee, smoking and alcohol are all major acid-producers. Consume a diet which is 80% alkali-ash-producing foods and 20% of everything else, *while dumping acid-producing behaviour*. You can dramatically change the way your body feels in as little as five days – I'll show you how in a minute (*see* **Free Up Your Digestive Cycles**).

Notice from the lists at the back of this book almost all fruits and veggies are alkali-ash-producing, *and yet many are acidic going in*. Even a humble pear will register pH5.5 before blast-off, and yet pears like apples have an alkalising effect on the body, provided they are eaten sparingly on their own and not combined with proteins or starches. Fruits, veggies, pulses and legumes are simply the best alkalising tools on the market, containing the essential minerals the body requires to set up its intricate buffer systems. If your tongue or mouth hurt when you consume fruit, you are acidic! Change your diet *gradually* using raw, unfired fruits and vegetables and your body will appreciate you for your care and attention.

My recipe book, *Food For Thought*, will set you up with some righteous nosh which tastes great and is easy to prepare. Of course, changing behaviour is challenging, even impossible for some, who are addicted to sugar-laden foods and rebel at the idea of a McKeith Make-Over. For you we have a special section in a minute to convince you to mend your wicked ways.

But before we move on ...

~ 94 ~
Get in the Raw

Raw fruits and veggies contain enzymes which are destroyed during cooking (over 45°C/118°F). Enzymes switch off healing processes. Cancer is a healing process that has not terminated upon completion of its task.[8] Join the dots and eat raw foods.

Prof. John Beard, Drs Harold Manner, Shelton, Krebs, Binzel, Contreras and others all found raw foods the critical issue for their patients' recovery from serious illness. They received some serious persecution when they wrote about it, yet what do we read on the wires today?

Good Diet Helps in Cancer Treatment

But very few sufferers are given any advice on how to improve what they eat [9]

Raw, organic foods in particular, bowing under the weight of vitamins, minerals and enzymes, assist the body in regaining health, sometimes when all hope for the patient has been lost. I myself have reported on numerous cases of 'terminally ill' folk making startling recoveries when diets are changed, minds focused on getting better, and doctor ministrations kept to a minimum (*see* **Choose the Right Doctor**). Somehow, the bland exhortations from the establishment to 'Eat your fruits and vegetables, kids!' just don't convey the correct sense of urgency about this most important icon.

---

[8] **Day, Phillip** *Cancer: Why We're Still Dying to Know the Truth*, Credence 2005

[9] *The Daily Telegraph*, 10th July 2006

Raw foods as God intended should be eaten the same way. Minimising sugar-yielding, processed, high-glycaemic carbohydrates like cakes, 'ready' meals (ready for the bin), pastas and other grain and potato derivatives in favour of real food will change the way you feel in a hurry. If you spend days feeling lethargic and listless, act now! Make a special effort to obtain organic produce. Some paint this as a chore - and sometimes it's hard to procure a quality supply - but this is food we're talking about - future bits of you - not a new bag for your vacuum-cleaner. Ensure raw foods play a part in your staple *every day* and encourage others to do the same.

Another bonus: *They taste great!*

~ 93 ~
Exercise – Walk 10,000 Steps a Day

'If God had intended us to be nudists, we would have been born with no clothes on.' - **Leonard Lyons**

Most people don't - exercise, I mean. Perhaps the combined abuse of the last three icons has caused the greatest anguish and illness in modern society: Rubbish food coupled with indolent, acidic lifestyles punctuated by unhealthy stress all seem a far cry from the farm-fresh produce and yomps on the Downs enjoyed by our forebears. The fact is, though times have moved on, the body's needs for nourishment and exercise have not. If we don't meet them we must expect trouble. Here are the exercise basics:

Walk 10,000 steps a day. For a couple of quid you can get a plastic pedometer from a sports store to clip onto your belt. Doing nothing all day but shuffling around in your pyjamas will clock up 3,800 steps (In the name of research, I measured it. Three days in a row). 10,000 steps will put a progressive load onto your muscle and cardio systems and ensure you stay well-oiled and piped. (see also: **Climb Stairs Whenever You Can** and **Own a Pet**).

Load-bearing exercise: The dreaded weight-training, push-ups, knee bends, squats and stair-climbing are all resistance moves that prevent the muscles and skeleton from atrophy. These movements pump the lymph system and help clean you out. Weight-training can be done by **all** ages, though kids under ten are better off with the usual chores, slavery and play until the body fills out and matures in its middle teens.

60-90 minutes a day spent outside. The body requires sunlight and fresh air to manufacture Vitamin D and catalyse other reactions. Solar radiation penetrates even that lead blanket over Kent, so don't think of using your weather as an excuse unless you live in New Orleans.

Motivation

Exercise is hard for many because exercise equals pain and the brain moves away from pain toward pleasure as part of the survival response. 'No pain, no gain' results in thousands of gym memberships being paid for and never used. Nike's famous slogan 'Just Do It!', frankly, for most people didn't. Why? 'No pain, no gain.' We like the idea of what exercise can do for us, it's just the grunting and heavy-breathing part most of us have a problem with.

Shift Your Focus

Don't call it exercise – ***play!*** Re-label and shift your focus. Get involved in a hobby that combines exercise with fun: walking, gardening, cycling, swimming. I like exploring battlefields and historical sites, so climbing mottes and nodding at baileys gets me all hot and bothered. Orienteering, rollerblading and fell-walking are great, but if you're getting on a bit, gardening, sponsored walks, swimming, cycling and invading France were all enjoyed by your antecedents.

- Exercising is easy if you're having fun (play)
- Remember: You are the sum total of everything you've ever done to yourself
- *Don't overlook exercise*

~ 92 ~
Free up Your Digestive Cycles

Want to feel good in just five days?

Embodied in the Principles of Longevity is the Science of Natural Hygiene. Natural Hygiene revolves around the following juicy topics:

- Understanding the body's natural digestive cycles
- Correct consumption of fruit
- The concept of high water-content food
- Correct food-combining
- Detoxification

The Body's Natural Digestive Cycles

Natural Hygiene teaches that the human body's digestive system goes through three, eight-hour cycles every twenty-four hours:

Noon - 8pm: **Appropriation** of food (eating and digestion)
8pm - 4am: **Assimilation** of food (absorption and use)
4am - Noon: **Elimination** (excretion of waste)

It isn't hard to see these cycles in action. It's also uncomfortably apparent when these cycles are thrown into turmoil by, for example, wolfing down a pizza late at night or machining your way through heart-attack-on-a-plate for breakfast, wondering why you're feeling so trog-like and slothful.

APPROPRIATION (12 noon - 8pm)

The eating cycle. The body prefers the Appropriation Cycle to happen on time, commencing at noon. From this point until 8pm, eat 80% out of a kitchen garden (alkali ash foods: most fruits, vegetables, pulses, legumes and haricots) and 20% of everything else (acid ash foods: meat, dairy, grains, etc.) Eat little, but often to regulate blood sugar. Then, after 8pm, push back from the trough and allow the body to enter its next phase ...

ASSIMILATION (8pm - 4am)

Assimilation occurs at night (nutrient extraction and use), which makes all the sense in the world since the body is resting and the digestive system can crank into gear with the minimum of disruption. Night-time is not a good time for Appropriation in view of the hour and horizontal angles involved.

During Assimilation, the body extracts nutrients in the intestines, which are designed to keep high-water-content, high-fibre, unrefined plant dietary in their clutches until the useable nutrients are withdrawn. If you leave two hours between your last meal and bed, a properly combined supper will have already departed the stomach and be on its peaceful way through the alimentary tract by the time you lay your precious head on the pillow. During the night, your body is putting all those nutrients to work replenishing your systems, replacing damaged cells and allowing the blood and lymph systems to pick up waste and take it to the garbage collection points.

ELIMINATION (4am - 12 noon)

Elimination cuts in around 4am and the garbage truck arrives to take out the junk (the poop cycle). Your body has sorted through all it has processed and rejected anything that cannot be absorbed and satisfactorily metabolised into new bits of you. Elimination is simply the removal of waste matter from the body, a highly efficient system, which uses the bowel and urine to excrete the junk the body no longer wants. The body also eliminates toxins via the underarm, groin area, nose, mouth, ears and skin. It's all a mess but it's leaving, and that's a good thing.

Needless to say, *Elimination is the most thwarted cycle of the three* - an abuse that has led to chronic obesity and catastrophic ill-health in our populations. The Elimination Cycle is almost always ridden off the road by big, badly combined, bully-breakfasts, which hamstring the body's digestive resources and prevent the proper excretion of toxins. Thus some remain within you and get filed in all the parts where they can do the least harm but be the most noticeable. Bad skin, bad breath, bad hair - we look with offence at our nakedness: *'Good grief, I look like a beached whale!'* Your body is naturally offended at the insult being aimed in its general direction and caustically replies: *'Then unplug me, Einstein, and let's get rid of the whale....'*

Take Action

Those with the wicked ways I mentioned earlier, try this to feel good in just *five days*: From the time of waking, forget 'breakfast' and just snack sparingly on fruit or have a vegetable juice up until noon. After that, you will become uncomfortable if you do not eat. The most important rule during Elimination (4 am - Noon) is to allow the body to cleanse itself and help it on its way with highly nutritious, enzyme-loaded fruits and veg. These will help normalise your blood sugar naturally, so you won't feel hungry. *Don't overdo the fruit.*

The recipes in *Food For Thought* are ideal for Natural Hygiene detoxification. Notice the morning component is not breakfast cereal, fried eggs, fried bread, half a pig, coffee, etc, *but fruit*. If you have *Candida* or other sugar-sensitive condition, cut back on the fruit (to just one apple and pear), and have a veggie juice or light salad instead until noon arrives and Appropriation begins.

Do just five days of aligning your cycles in this way and tell me you don't feel like snapping telephone poles in half with your bare hands. Getting lean but not mean is a matter of continuing in this paragon endeavour even after you start seeing the benefits. I like fast but genuine results in looking and feeling good. Give this a try.

NEXT!

See also:

You Are What You Eat
Eat Raw Food
Eat Small Meals Often
Do a Bowel Cleanse
Drink Two Litres of Water a Day

- 91 -
Choose the Right Doctor

'There must be something to acupuncture - after all, you never see any sick porcupines.' - **Bob Goddard**

Unnecessary surgeries, drug-prescribing, unneeded tests and dangerous treatments all contribute to a frightening toll wrought by doctors around the world today. My book *Health Wars* documents the phenomenon of 'death by doctoring' in detail, and reveals the reasons why, while medicine has made great advances in certain areas, (infant survival, A & E trauma medicine, wound surgery, etc) and should justifiably receive the credit, it has failed miserably in others, most notably, 'mental health' and the treatment of disease. These failures are largely due to the belief that treating symptoms with drugs is the same thing as curing the disease itself, which it isn't.

Examples:

- Painkillers to treat hangovers, which are a dehydration issue
- The removal of tumours in the belief this will cure cancer
- The treatment of behavioural 'disorders' using drugs to mask symptoms
- Hysterectomies to cure menopausal woes
- Electroshock treatment (ECT) to cure mental illness

Most diseases such as cancer, heart disease, diabetes, arthritis, are metabolic (systemic) conditions related to diet and lifestyle, yet doctors are not trained in nutrition. Doctors are instead compelled to swallow the most extraordinary paradox that food is apparently good enough to keep you alive but not good enough to fix you when you're sick. Many I've interviewed over the years are fed up to the back teeth with this crummy state of affairs and wish to see things changed. They did not go into medicine not to heal people. Most conventional doctors, if they're honest, will admit they can't heal their patients' diseases.[10]

Facts:

- You are what you eat
- Food can change your mood
- Every cell in your body comes from what you ingest
- A New You is produced approximately every seven years after all your old cells have died out and been replaced with new ones. The quality of the New You and how well it will function will be down to diet and lifestyle, with genetics playing an adjunctive role

Bad diets in hospitals only contribute to the difficulties patients experience in overcoming illness. MRSA and other infections strike patients who have compromised immunity. What we should do is fire the hospital dieticians, retool the kitchens to produce tasty, raw, nutritious whole-foods, train our doctors and nurses in nutrition, and do all we can to boost patients' immunity with adequate hydration, hope and mental stimulation. Not drug them up and leave them sitting in front of Paul O'Grady on the TV with their bread and milk.

The current, drug-based, medical approach to disease:

- Is failing and dangerous
- Pays no heed to prevention
- Lacks proper nutrition support completely

---

[10] **Hammond, Phil** *Trust Me, I'm a Doctor,* Metro Books, 1999

- Prefers the bullish use of surgical or chemical intervention
- Views illness as a collection of localised symptoms to be treated with drugs/surgery rather than banishing the underlying causation with lifestyle and dietary changes

Viz:

ISRAELI DOCTORS GO ON STRIKE AND DEATH RATES PLUMMET

'Death rates in Israel have dropped considerably since physicians in public hospitals implemented a program of sanctions three months ago, according to a survey of burial societies.

The Israel Medical Association (IMA) began the action in March to protest against the government's proposed imposition of a new four-year wage contract for doctors. Since then, hundreds of thousands of visits to outpatient clinics have been canceled or postponed along with tens of thousands of elective operations. Emergency rooms, dialysis units, oncology departments, obstetric and neonatal departments, and other vital facilities have been working normally during the action.

The Jerusalem Post surveyed non-profit burial societies, which perform funerals for the vast majority of Israelis, and found that the number of funerals has fallen drastically.

According to one funeral parlor manager the same thing occurred in 1983, during a similar action by the IMA, which lasted 4 and a half months.

The only area of Israel which was found to not have a reduction in its death rate was the city of Netanya. It also just so happens that all of the doctors at the only hospital in this city have "no-strike" clauses in their contracts and are therefore unaffected by the action.'[11]

In Short

No-one's suggesting you don't need a doctor. I am suggesting you might exercise reasonable caution before swallowing everything Nurse shoves down your throat. When assessing your needs for a doctor, fall back on those good old bastions of reason, logic and common sense:

- Prevention is the best cure
- Better not to get sick in the first place
- Change your attitude, diet and lifestyle
- Just do it!
- Ensure the family is well fed with a varied intake of wholesome, nutritious, *organic* foods
- Reduce stress
- Be happy
- Consult a doctor who gives advice on lifestyle and diet

Fact: *Correct* drug prescribing is the largest sub-sector of iatrogenic (doctor-induced) deaths in most First World countries.[12]

---

[11] www.mercola.com; British Medical Journal 2000;320:1561

[12] **Day, Phillip** *Health Wars*, op. cit.

- 90 -
Put Plants Around the Place

Plants are good for you - official.

- Not for nothing is gardening one of the more popular pastimes. The reason? Relaxation, reflection and worms
- Caring for plants (caring's the important bit) causes us to project outside ourselves, drags us out of our self-obsessive problems to help another organic life-form in its struggle for survival
- Plants filter pollutants given off by modern, synthetic materials used in homes and offices. Emissions of formaldehyde, benzene, hexane, xylene, toluene and ammonia have all been found to reduce in the presence of healthy greenery, some by up to 100% in 24 hours in a closed environment [13]
- Dr Joseph Mercola reports: *'NASA scientists... found houseplants can actually extract volatile organic chemicals (VOCs) from the air. According to one study, one six-inch houseplant per 100 square feet of indoor area acts as a decent filter for the air, and another U.S. government study found that 15 to 18 houseplants in six- to eight-inch containers helps improve the air quality in an 1,800-square-foot house'* [14]
- In designing a breathable environment for a NASA lunar habitat, Dr B C Wolverton discovered that toxic chemicals in closed, indoor environments with poor ventilation often triggered 'Sick Building Syndrome', featuring a host of

---

[13] www.mercola.com

[14] Ibid.

respiratory and allergic reactions. These could often be relieved by purifying the environment with any one of 50 house plants noted for their filtration abilities [15]

- In their book, *The Secret Life of Plants,* authors Peter Tomkins and Christopher Bird go a quantum leap further in reporting the experiments conducted by CIA scientist Cleve Backster into the 'Backster Effect' - how plants respond to human emotions, both positive and negative.[16] Richard Klein, Professor of Botany at Vermont University, remarks: *'Plants and men do interrelate, with plants exhibiting empathetic and spiritual relationships and showing reactions interpreted as demonstrating physical-force connections with men. As my students say, 'Wow!''*

Yes, well, put plants around the place.

[15] **Wolverton, B C** *How to Grow Fresh Air, 50 House Plants that Purify Your Home and Office,* Penguin, 1996

[16] **Tompkins and Bird** *The Secret Life of Plants,* Harper and Row, 1989

~ 89 ~
Lose the Mobile Phone

Me, two years ago: Can't get a thing done. Each call that comes in triggers two more. People can get me on the toilet, send photos of their tongue sticking out. I get burning temples, ringing ears and big bills. There must be an easier way.

There was. I tossed the phone.

By getting a mobile phone I had inadvertently:

A) increased the spin of my hamster wheel
B) wrecked any chance of getting my goals accomplished
C) introduced an unhealthy dollop of site-specific radiation to my lug-hole
D) increased the chances of getting mugged, not least by unscrupulous phone-company tariffs

A mobile phone makes a spontaneous demand on your time. The more calls, the more distraction. I route everything these days via e-mail, which means I can deal with it when I want, and folks get my reply written down, which I hope is better.

Then there's the radiation. Do a search on my site at **www.credence.org** for the problems of brain tumours, living in proximity to mast installations, and the dreaded cordless. The best way to decide this issue is to gauge your usage.

Some Tips

- Two calls a day - no problem
- Twenty calls a day - problem
- Don't use a cordless house phone
- Don't use a mobile unless you have to
- Ensure you live at least 200 yards away from a mast installation
- Don't use those Captain Kirk ear-pieces. There's nothing convenient about strutting around frying your brain in public
- Don't sleep with a mobile switched on beside your bed
- Check the house for other sources of electro-magnetic radiation (EMF) smog: plug sockets by the pillow, TVs on stand-by, microwaves, computers, laptops, etc.
- Try going four weeks without the mobile and get addicted to the peace
- Review **credence.org**, **mastsanity.org** and **mercola.com** for more information on this subject (you can search by keyword)

- 88 -
Limit Caffeine, Alcohol and Carbonated Drinks

Alas, some things are rotten for us, and we live in an age where if a little is good, more must be much better. A later chapter, **There is Danger in Excess, Moderation in All Things**, is a motto directly applicable to the Parlour Room Three. Let's find out what the problems are.

Caffeine

... is the most widely used drug in the world. It perks us up by stimulating the body into producing adrenalin to generate temporary stress. The fight-or-flight response is supposed to be just that - temporary (the length of time it takes to wrestle Matron to the ground). However, many become addicted to how caffeine changes their psychological state from perceived pain ('Oh dear - morning') to a state of action ('Right, let's get on with it'), and thereby get drawn into a day-long usage of it. I think the beverage industry knows this.

Excess stress depletes Vitamin C, provides the conditions for plaque to generate in the arteries (atherosclerosis/scurvy), reduces iron absorption and degrades mental performance.[17] Caffeine has been linked to increased risk of stroke[18] and rheumatoid arthritis.[19] Caffeine also reduces insulin sensitivity so

---

[17] See *ABC's of Disease,* heart section.
Also, http://www.tribuneindia.com/2000/20001029/spectrum/fitness.htm

[18] *Journal of Clinical Epidemiology,* 1998;51:487-494.

[19] *Annals of the Rheumatic Diseases,* 2000;59;631-635.

we don't process sugars as efficiently, which can lead to insulin resistance and diabetes.[20] A cup of coffee in the morning is not what I'm talking about. Five cups a day is.

Chronic coffee drinkers are surfing the bean - hate to say it, but it's a drug addiction. Try giving it up and you'll witness all the evidence of addiction withdrawal. Some of the unpleasantness is down to the caffeine, the rest attributable to mental patterning/comfort zones we have installed (*see* **Deal With Addictions**). Try switching to tart vegetable juices when you get up - much better for you and the nutrients help overcome caffeine cravings (see **Juice Veggies**). Disrupt your mental patterning by changing your morning routine to avoid the breakfast table (see **Free up Your Digestive Cycles**). Exercise aerobically with a brisk walk or jog after you get up (remember to stretch); your body is craving oxygen, not a cappuccino with cinnamon and a chocolate torpedo. If you are a coffee, alcohol *and* carbonated beverage quaffer, you've probably got reflux (heartburn) and some digestive issues by now, even more so if you're a smoker. Change your wicked ways!

But... But...

If you really must drink coffee, Dr Joseph Mercola offers the following useful pointers:

- ***Use organic coffee*** *- Coffee is a heavily sprayed crop, so drinking organic coffee might reduce or eliminate the exposure to toxic herbicides, pesticides, and fertilizers. The only drawback is that the countries where coffee is produced probably have less control and monitoring for compliance to*

---

[20] **Diabetes Care**, February 2002;25:364-369

organic practices. You will also be helping to protect the health of the people working in the coffee fields, as you will be helping to reduce their toxic exposure as well

- ***"Swiss Water Process" decaf*** *- If you are going to drink decaffeinated coffee, be sure that it is one that uses a non-chemical-based method of decaffeination. The "Swiss Water Process" is a patented method and the best choice. Most of the major brands are chemically decaffeinated, even if it says "Naturally Decaffeinated" on the container. If you are unsure of the methods, contact the manufacturer*
- ***Avoid sugar and/or milk*** *- These are actually much worse for you than the coffee itself. Don't compound the detrimental health effects by adding milk or sugar to your coffee*
- ***Unbleached filters*** *- If you use a "drip" coffee-maker, be sure to use non-bleached filters. The bright white ones, which most people use, are chlorine-bleached and some of this chlorine will be extracted from the filter during the brewing process*

Alcohol

Once again it's a matter of scale. Alcohol is a cell-poison. A glass of red wine a day has shown antioxidant benefits, but not because of the alcohol![21] The danger with any mood-changers lies in the perceived change in state from 'pain' to 'pleasure', which tempts us into renewing the high. Bound up with addiction is the denial issue, the protective mechanism the brain uses against the anticipated pain of withdrawal. If that's you in any area of addiction, rule number one: *Don't justify what's hurting you.* Rule number two: *Get help* (*see* **Deal With Addictions**).

---

[21] www.americanheart.org

Carbonated Drinks

Sally Squires reports: *'Americans drink more soda pop* [fizzy drinks] *than ever before. These popular beverages account for more than a quarter of all drinks consumed in the United States. More than 15 billion gallons were sold in 2000. That works out to at least one 12-ounce can per day for every man, woman and child.*

Kids are heavy consumers of soft drinks, according to the U.S. Department of Agriculture, and they are guzzling soda pop at unprecedented rates. Carbonated soda pop provides more added sugar in a typical 2-year-old toddler's diet than cookies, candies and ice cream combined. Fifty-six percent of 8-year-olds down soft drinks daily, and a third of teenage boys drink at least three cans of soda pop per day.

Not only are soft drinks widely available everywhere, from fast food restaurants to video stores, they're now sold in 60 percent of all public and private middle schools and high schools nationwide, according to the National Soft Drink Association. A few schools are even giving away soft drinks to students who buy school lunches.

As soda pop becomes the beverage of choice among the nation's young - and as soda marketers focus on brand-building among younger and younger consumers - public health officials, school boards, parents, consumer groups and even the soft drink industry are faced with nagging questions:

How healthful are these beverages, which provide a lot of calories, sugars and caffeine but no significant nutritional value?

And what happens if you drink a lot of them at a very young age?"[22]

Well, it's not good. Carbonated drinks are acidic and cause oesophageal reflux. The carbonation process, as its name implies, uses carbon dioxide in a medium of phosphoric acid. Though carbonation is alluring by dint of its 'thirst-quenching' properties, real thirst-quenching is accomplished using water not acid. Many of the diet versions of these drinks are also 'sweetened' with aspartame, a neurological toxin,[23] while those that aren't can contain anywhere from six to ten teaspoons of sugar. And if that isn't enough, phosphorous depletes calcium, which leads to bone loss, the condition known as osteoporosis.

Summary

In a perfect world, we would do without the lot and just drink water. Am I kidding? No. However, advertising and the taste monster have conspired to seduce an entire planet, so I suspect the reality for most of us will be a casual usage somewhere in between.

My advice? Try doing without them or set strict limits on use and ruthlessly enforce. These three can be an addictive, lethal deluge of acid (not to mention all the chemicals and preservatives involved). When ill-advisedly combined with a stressful, busy lifestyle and maintained over the long-haul? See **Choose the Right Doctor**.

---

[22] http://www.mercola.com/2001/mar/10/soda_pop_dangers.htm

[23] See *The ABC's of Disease:* Aspartame Disease.

- 87 -
Supplement Real Vitamin C

Dr Linus Pauling, known as the 'Father of Vitamin C' and twice awarded the Nobel Prize, declared that daily intakes of this vitamin complex aid anti-cancer activity and assist in repairing damaged arteries and removing arterial plaque (atherosclerosis). Pauling was largely derided for making these declarations (he lived to be 94!), but today, large doses of Vitamin C complex are used by many practitioners to great effect who believe Pauling was right and that the popular nutrient is indispensable to the body in its fight to regain or maintain health.

An associate of Pauling's, Dr Matthias Rath, writes:

'Animals don't get heart attacks because they produce Vitamin C in their bodies, which protects their blood vessel walls. In humans, unable to produce Vitamin C (a condition known as hypoascorbemia), dietary vitamin deficiency weakens these walls. Cardiovascular disease is an early form of scurvy. Clinical studies document that optimum daily intakes of vitamins and other essential nutrients halt and reverse coronary heart disease naturally.

The single most important difference between the metabolism of human beings and most other living species is the dramatic difference in the body pool of Vitamin C. The body reservoir of Vitamin C in people is on average 10 to 100 times lower than the Vitamin C levels in animals.' [24]

---

[24] **Rath, Matthias**, *Why Animals Don't Get Heart Attacks - But People Do!* MR Publishing, 2000, p.10

Pauling and Rath reported:

- Optimum Vitamin C intake should be 600 mg - 3 g daily (depending on bodyweight and stress levels), along with supportive intakes of Vitamin E (600 - 1,000 IU), the amino acids lysine and proline, the B vitamins, essential fatty acids (EFAs), magnesium, minerals, trace minerals and amino acids to provide healthy arteries
- A long-term Vitamin C deficiency will lead to atherosclerotic deposits in the arterial walls to cover the breaches caused by the disintegrating collagen, resulting in coronary heart disease and, further north, strokes to the brain
- Vitamin C depletion over a few months will lead to massive blood loss through collagen disintegration, resulting in leaky artery walls, collapsing organs and death by scurvy[25]

Dr G C Willis demonstrated Vitamin C complex could reverse atherosclerosis. Willis gave a sample of his patients 1.5 grams of Vitamin C a day and gave the remainder no Vitamin C at all. After a year, the atherosclerotic deposits in the patients fed the Vitamin C had decreased in 30% of the cases. In contrast, no reduction in deposits was observed in the control group, which had grown further. Sadly, in spite of the clear evidence over 40 years ago of the benefits of just Vitamin C through Willis' work, no follow-up study was ever commissioned.[26]

Professor Gey, from the University of Basel in Switzerland, conducted studies in which he compared the Vitamin C, Vitamin A (beta carotene) and cholesterol intakes of citizens living in

---

[25] Ibid.

[26] **Willis GC, Light AW & WS Gow**, "Serial arteriography in atherosclerosis", *Canadian Medical Association Journal* (1954) 71: pp.562-568

Northern Europe with their counterparts in the southern regions of the continent. He found:

- Those living in the northern nations had the highest levels of cardiovascular disease and lowest blood levels of vitamins
- Southern European populations had the reverse statistics of their northern counterparts and were much more healthy
- Optimum intakes of vitamins C, E and A had far greater impact on decreasing risks of cardiovascular disease than the reduction of cholesterol, now becoming increasingly viewed (correctly) as a secondary factor in heart-disease risk (an inevitable result of the primary deficiency of nutrients leading to the breakdown of arterial walls)

Gey's report also highlighted the preference for the Mediterranean diet, rich in wine and olive oil, abundant in bioflavonoids (a part of the C complex) and Vitamin E as a main prevention regimen for heart disease in almost all its forms.[27]

Further studies showed that these nutrients separately produced impressive results for cardiac disease prevention:

- Vitamin C intake lowers cardiovascular risk by 50%[28] [29]

---

[27] **Gey KF, Puska P, Jordan P & UK Moser**, "Inverse correlation between plasma Vitamin E and mortality from ischemic heart disease in cross-cultural epidemiology" *American Journal of Clinical Nutrition* (1991) 53: p.326, supplement

[28] **Ginter E**, "Vitamin C deficiency cholesterol metabolism and atherosclerosis" *Journal of Orthomolecular Medicine* (1991) 6:pp.166-173; **Ginter E**, "Marginal Vitamin C deficiency, lipid metabolism and atherosclerosis" *Lipid Research* (1978) 16: pp.216-220

[29] **Harwood HJ Jr, Greene YJ & PW Stacpoole**, "Inhibition of human leucocyte 3-hydroxy-3-methylglutaryl coenzyme A reductase activity by ascorbic acid. An

- Vitamin E intake lowers cardiovascular risk by one-third, documented in 87,000 study participants over six years[30]
- Beta carotene (Vitamin A) intake lowers cardiovascular risk over 30%, documented in more than 87,000 study participants over six years
- No prescription drug has ever come close to matching these figures in preventing heart disease[31]

However, when these nutrients were combined with other synergistic agents, such as magnesium, Vitamin B3 (nicotinic acid), Vitamin B5 (pantothenate) and the amino acid carnitine, and levels of these maintained in the body over the long-term, near total prevention could be expected, and in those already suffering from a variety of cardiac ailments, a clear record of efficacy in reversing these conditions was consistently observed. [32] [33] [34] [35]

Scurvy in the industrial nations is almost an impossibility (Vitamin C depletion), even with the ghastly diets with which we

---

effect mediated by the free radical monodehydro-ascorbate" *Journal of Biological Chemistry* (1986) 261: pp.7127-7135

[30] **Beamish R**, "Vitamin E - then and now" *Canadian Journal of Cardiology* (1993) 9: pp. 29-31

[31] Rath, Matthias, op. cit. p.53

[32] **Sokolov B, Hori M, Saelhof CC, Wrzolek T & T Imai**, "Aging, atherosclerosis and ascorbic acid metabolism" *Journal of the American Gerontology Society* (1966) 14: 1239-1260

[33] **Opie LH**, "Role of carnitine in fatty acid metabolism of normal and ischemic myocardium" *American Heart Journal* (1979) 97: pp.375-388

[34] **Avogaro P, Bon GB & M Fusello**, "Effect of pantethine on lipids, lipoproteins and apolipoproteins in man" *Current Therapeutic Research* (1983) 33: pp.488-493

[35] **Altschul R, Hoffer A & JD Stephen**, "Influence of nicotinic acid on serum cholesterol in man" *Archives of Biochemistry and Biophysics* (1955) 54: pp.558-559; **Carlson LA, Hamsten A & A Asplund**, "Pronounced lowering of serum levels of lipoprotein Lp(a) in hyperlipidemic subjects treated with nicotinic acid" *Journal of Internal Medicine (England)* (1989) 226: 271-276

feed ourselves. However, long-term C *deficiency* is common in many, hence the prevalence of heart disease and stroke in their various forms today.

Vitamin C is not just ascorbic acid, it's a complex of factors common in fruits, vegetables and other foods. Several studies have suggested that Vitamin C may reduce levels of lead in the blood. Epidemiological studies have shown that people with elevated blood serum levels of C had lower levels of blood toxicity. An examination of the data from the Third National Health and Nutrition Examination Survey, enrolling 4,213 youths aged 6 to 16 years and 15,365 adults 17 years and older from 1988 to 1994, found a correlation between low serum ascorbic acid levels and elevated blood lead levels. The authors concluded high ascorbic acid intake may reduce blood lead levels.[36]

Ascorbic acid or the non-acidic ascorbates (calcium or magnesium ascorbates) should be taken with bioflavonoids along with a healthy, alkalising diet for optimum effects. Dosage recommended by Pauling/Rath for prevention is between 600mg and 3g a day, or up to 10g/day for those with cancer. Extremely high levels of C can cause diarrhoea and be contraindicated with certain chemotherapy treatments.

VITAMIN P (bioflavonoids): another part of the Vitamin C 'complex'. Dr Albert Szent-Gyorgi, 1937 Nobel Laureate for his isolation of Vitamin C, later found other factors intrinsic to its action. Originally believed to be a single nutrient, Vitamin C became the subject of further testing by Szent-Gyorgi, who fought hard to have the co-factor (bio)flavonoids included in the

---

[36] **Simon JA, Hudes ES**, "Relationship of Ascorbic Acid to Blood Lead Levels" *Journal of the American Medical Association*, 1999;281:2289-2293

description. Coining the new bioflavonoids 'Vitamin P', Szent-Gyorgi argued they were essential for proper body function, derived from plant pigments known as the flavonols and flavones. Bioflavonoids are widely accepted today for their health benefits and are available in hydroxylated and methoxylated forms. They are derived from the pith of fruits (mostly citrus). Quercetin, rutin, catechin, anthocyanidins and proanthocyanidins are examples of flavonoids and are great-sounding names. 'Vitamin P', however, was less well received by our medical czars.

Summary

I have been supplementing powdered, bioflavonoid C complex for years and enjoy paramount health (see **Use a Basic Supplement Program**). Finding a decent C supplement that is *not* just ascorbic acid and *not* in tablet form (avoid the binders and fillers) has proved a bit of a trial, however. We have since developed a highly successful C product in cahoots with manufacturers in the Netherlands, so if you're stuck for the best stuff and fed up with burning holes in your tum with ascorbic acid, log on to www.credence.org and order some online.

Postscript

Of course, Vitamin C is great insurance, but there is no substitute for real food. Eating a balanced diet rich in these factors, reducing stress, adopting a positive outlook and exercising regularly will cover most of the bases.

- 86 -

Get a Hobby

'Miss Marcia Devin sang 'I Will Not Pass This Way Again', giving obvious pleasure to the entire congregation.' - **Leo Rosten**

One of the best stress-relievers going is to get a hobby. Aside from my work at Credence, my hobbies are writing novels, researching arcane subjects such as Saxon England, and flying large-scale, radio-controlled aircraft.

Unlike most jobs where you show up and look interested merely to exchange your most precious resource (time) for money, the great thing about a hobby is that it stimulates your *real* interest, your action, your involvement - you were the one who chose it in the first place, remember?

A hobby, according to Websters, is a medium-sized, vigorous horse. Also something you like to do or study in your spare time. Aside from being cracking good fun, hobbies break up the geographic concentration of stress (work, home, etc.) and act as a safety valve. *Hobbies don't have to mean anything.* I have a workshop I retire to where I build planes. My playpen is off-limits to the world because that's where I go to get away from it all. Once a plane is built, it gets engine- and radio-tested, put in the back of the van, driven down to Romney Marsh where I've use of some fenland. Then it's a matter of clearing the sheep off the runway, getting the thing started and taking to the friendly skies, or taking the bits home in a bin-bag, whatever the outcome.

The point is, all the while I'm doing that, I'm not doing this.

That's called a break.

Lot's of people don't have a hobby.

Not sure what you can do? Visit a bookstore and find out what everyone else is doing! Create, serve, paint, polish, act, visit, sing, dance or blissfully close your eyes to the multiple roar of P-38 engines.

See also:
You're Never Too Old to Change
Time is Your Most Precious Resource
Never Retire
Laugh a Lot
Take a Four-Week Holiday
Don't Lose Your Joy
Create Overwhelming Optimistic Experiences
Reward Yourself
Live One Day at a Time
Dare to Dream
Be Inspired
Avoid Dreamkillers
Be Thankful

- 85 -

Get a Pet

(And care for them!)

'I spilt spot-remover on my dog. He's gone now.' - **Steve Wright**

Pets are also good for you - official.

Researchers at the State Universities of New York at Buffalo and California at Santa Barbara discovered pet-owners had *'significantly lower heart rate and blood pressure levels during a resting baseline, significantly smaller increases (ie, reactivity) from baseline levels during the mental arithmetic and cold pressor, and faster recovery. Among pet owners, the lowest reactivity and quickest recovery was observed in the pet-present conditions'.* [37]

In regular language, Fifi can do the following:

- Provide company
- Be there when you get home
- Get you out of the house for walkies (budgies, I'm not sure)
- Care
- Rely on you
- Cause you to project outside your own worries to care for them
- Reduce your stress and blood-pressure

---

[37] **Allen, Karen, Blascovich, Jim & Wendy B Mendes**, "Cadiovascular reactivity and the presence of pets, friends and spouses: The truth about cats and dogs" *Psychosomatic Medicine* 64:727-739 (2002)

Ensuring your pets are fed and cared for properly is the therapy. Dogs and cats are carnivores, which means they eat mainly *raw* meat, not the swill served up by the pet-food industry. Pet experts Steve Brown and Beth Taylor, authors of *See Spot Live Longer*,[38] argue the over-consumption of commercial grains, together with impromptu treats and 'doggie bags', could be sentencing your hound or lion to a fat, miserable, foreshortened existence. In the USA,

- Cancer is the number one disease killer of dogs
- One in three dogs will die from cancer
- 50 percent of dogs over the age of 10 will succumb to cancer

Dr Joseph Mercola, who quotes these statistics, states: *'Based on philosophies that mirror my own regarding the importance of nutrition, authors Beth Taylor and Steve Brown present evidence that good diets are just as important for dogs as they are for humans. They provide a convincing thesis for feeding your dog a naturally balanced raw meat, bone and vegetable-based diet that provides much higher quality nutrition than any dry or canned dog or cat food.*

Dry pet food manufacturers claim everything our animals need is inside that attractive bag with their beautiful pictures of meats, vegetables and fruits labeled "natural!" This would be great but it's impossible to make such claims. No matter how good the ingredients are in a bag of dog or cat food, it is still a highly processed, grain-based food, lacking in live, whole nutrients.'[39]

---

[38] www.mercola.com

[39] Ibid.

Of course, your cat's been trying to tell you this for years, bringing you dead pigeons and laying them at your feet: *'See? Two claws and a beak is what I eat, what's the problem?'*

Sober Analysis

- Carnivores don't cook in the wild
- They don't possess combine harvesters to gather grains
- They don't miscombine proteins and carbohydrates ('Rarely do you see a lion eating a zebra and having a baked potato with it' - Harvey Diamond)[40]
- Fish oils are good for carnivores, containing intelligence-enhancing DHA and EPA[41]
- Dogs dig their heels in when you try dragging them to the vet (learn from that)
- Dogs and cats spent the formative years of their history scavenging rotting scraps and devouring carcasses. Not a pleasant thought if you live in Chertsey, but true
- Understanding your pet's requirements and serving them well gets you a whole lot of lovin' in return
- Be a parent!

See also:

You're Never Too Old to Change
Laugh a Lot
Don't Lose Your Joy
Create Overwhelming Optimistic Experiences
Breathe Clean Air
Reward Yourself
Live One Day at a Time

---

[40] **Diamond, Harvey and Marilyn**, *Fit For Life*, Bantam, 2004
[41] AdAge.com, 26th July 2004

- 84 -

Get Out of Debt

'I haven't reported my missing credit card to the police because whoever stole it is spending less than my wife.'

- Ilie Nastase

One of the major stressors in modern life is debt. I am constantly amazed how little students are taught about managing finances properly, and I was no exception. Thrown into the bear-pit of the late 20th Century after a great college education, I had little or no experience in credit, debt, borrowing, hire purchase or balancing my cheque book. Surprisingly, credit was easy to get and I was soon in trouble, and apparently I wasn't the only one. And I think the banks know this. Here's what I learned.

- Avoid banks where possible
- Use cash wherever possible
- Taking out a loan or any form of debt needs to be thought through carefully
- Mortgages are OK (you're purchasing an appreciating asset), so long as the repayments are manageable and the property valued correctly
- Never, never, never consolidate your debt with another debt and put your house up as collateral. If you do, *buy a tent*
- Avoid using credit cards
- Credit should not be used to purchase items such as food, petrol, clothes, cars, holidays, etc. Most folks don't clear their card balances each month and so end up paying interest on old meals, consumables and depreciating assets for the next 246 years

- If possible, *lease* your car, *don't* own a depreciating asset that will never again be worth what you paid for it. Leasing is generally reserved for those with good credit since the equity remains with the bank and you make a lower payment in return
- Don't buy the car at the end of a lease unless you intend running it into the ground. It's an 80,000 mile piece of junk by this time with no warranty. NEVER finance the balloon payment (residual). Best thing is to hand the keys back, walk away and lease a new vehicle with a new warranty (this cuts down on repair bills too)
- The worst thing in the world is 'hire purchase'. Avoid, avoid, avoid (you're *owning* a depreciating asset)
- Personal debt is the most common form of financial stress. Some even pay their credit balances with other cards and wonder why they accumulate the national debt of a small country
- Live within your means. Materialists rarely gain spiritual satisfaction
- You will be in trouble if you cannot put a little away regularly
- The answer to a money problem is money, not Prozac or a Valium dependency
- Getting out of debt involves increasing your income and reducing your cost (standard) of living, preferably at the same time
- Don't loan money to individuals or friends, you'll lose both
- I don't invest in equities, pensions, bonds, mutuals or similar palaver, having seen too many lose their shirts to cowboy brokers
- I don't need a pension because I don't intend retiring (see **Never Retire**). I do have disability insurance, however, just in case. I intend to continue working and being productive right up until my requirement for oxygen ceases. Not only will I be

gainfully employed and glad of the money, I won't be vegetating in front of the TV snorting Cheese-Its, relying on state hand-outs which long since stopped keeping pace with rate of inflation

- I invest in property and my own skills, providing both are a going concern. There's a much higher return *and* you retain control of the action

Becoming debt-free is an attitude of mind.

Start working on your attitude today!

See also:
Be an Overcomer
Don't Be Dysfunctional Around Money

- 83 -
Think Good Thoughts, Don't Dwell on Evil

'Every time a child says, 'I don't believe in fairies', there's a little fairy somewhere that falls down dead.' – **J Barrie**

Do you suffer from impromptu, evil imaginings?

Disturbing thoughts that pop into your head?

Where on earth do they come from?

Seventy years ago, depictions of Blockbuster atrocities could only have been experienced on a field of battle. These days, horror is a multi-billion dollar industry celebrated daily as 'entertainment' and 'news'. Remember that repetition establishes the pattern in a state of emotion and that's what these thoughts are – a regurgitation of what you've been plugging your head into for the past twenty-five years.

I receive e-mails from those so afflicted. The world is a deadly and terrifying place, they tell me, every day brings more chaos and mayhem, you only need to watch the news or read the newspapers to see it. Well, don't watch the news or read the newspapers and you won't see it. A newscaster's job is to peddle disaster while Hollywood's job is to make fictional experiences as real as it can. Marlon Brando's doomed character sums it all up in *Apocalypse Now: 'The horror. The horror.'*

Ask what is real *for you.* Frightening experiences can be a fact of life, but how many times does real horror play a part in *your* life, apart from the cheese and pickle sandwiches they serve up at Charing Cross station in the rush hour? Our forebears would return from war muttering fragments of what they'd been through, but mostly wanted to get the horror behind them and look to the future. They educated their minds to overwrite such patterning by getting on with their lives and guarding input - not in such terms did they think it, they just persevered and were consistent, so it worked for most of them (*see* **Guard Input**). It's come to something when we can pick up a newspaper today and experience all the bad news in the world dumped on our breakfast table and never once question why we do it. *Because we really need to know?* (*see* **Avoid National Media**).

So, the antidote: Cut off the duff input. Think good thoughts. Develop a belief system that sees Good checking the advance of Evil. You have a choice about what you allow yourself to see and think, so try an experiment. Spend four weeks flooding your senses with nothing but good news, laughter and optimism. By the time you realise the experiment has worked, Pavlov's Principle will already have established a new, more benign pattern for your future.

Jealously guard your senses.

Be consistent in experiencing good.

See also:
Guard Input
Avoid National Media
The Sky Rarely Falls In
Turn Off the TV
Create Overwhelming Optimistic Experiences

~ 82 ~
Avoid Accidents
70% of accidents occur within five miles of the home. So move ten miles away

Two points I'd like to make on this one.

1) Take prudent precautions daily
2) And a pox on the Health and Safety Executive, *stop telling me how safe I've got to be!*

Prudent Precautions

Sometimes people die foolishly. In America, car crashes are the leading cause of death for Americans under 35. Tragically, such disasters almost always occur because of some routine oversight, distraction or a precaution not being taken. Mobile phones, fatigue, an insect (a big one) entering the car, unrestrained pets, children and other life-forms messing around in the back seat.[42] No belt on.

If you're attentive and sensible whenever embarking on something dangerous, obviously you will reduce the chances of accidents. For instance, seat-belt, look before pulling out, toss the mobile phone into the gym bag, etc. (*Do I really need to go over this?*) Driving becomes so routine for most of us, we leap into the hot-seat without much thought as to how the journey could end. Passing a smouldering wreck on the side of the motorway muttering *'There, but for the grace of God, go I'* is not quite the same as taking precautions. By the way, slowing down to gawp at

---

[42] *The Washington Post*, 17th March 2003

accidents (American, 'rubbernecking') is the leading cause of accidents in the US.

The Other Side of the Coin

I don't believe the universe is out to get me. I do believe in taking precautions. That having been said, I strenuously object to those pettifogging local government apparatchiks passing a blizzard of directives to save me from a) myself, b) from all the risks life might chuck at me, and c), jacking up my taxes to pay for all this nannying. And complaining makes me a Philistine, of course, after all, who doesn't want kids to be safe, right?

- Some schools have banned egg and spoon races in case the little darlings lose
- Cross-country running is now officially child abuse (that was the whole point) [43]
- A school in Kent has banned children from flying paper aeroplanes in case they'll have someone's eye out
- At a school in Middlesex, pre-teen pupils are told they'll each be given a courgette so that the purpose of a condom can be simulated. One scholar speaks for all when she asks: 'What's a courgette?'

Adults are too thick and stupid to watch out for themselves too. For the record, I reserve the right to ride my bicycle without one of those alien-badger-plastic-nasties on my head. I'll walk my dog in the park without a lead - at her age, Rosie is far more likely to *suck* a kid to death. Apparently all of us are now such a danger to each other that we are in need of 24-hour legislative

---

[43] *Daily Mail,* 7th August 2006

protection. So politicians dream up ever more horrible ways to be busy and lawyers get rich, so *cui bono?*

Can you legislate the risk out of life? Of course not.

US Congressman (person) Ron Paul sniffs a rodent: *'Freedom is not defined by safety, Freedom is defined by the ability of citizens to live without government interference. Government cannot create a world without risks, nor would we really wish to live in such a fictional place. Only a totalitarian society would even claim absolute safety as a worthy ideal because it would require total state control over its citizens' lives. This doesn't stop governments, including our own, from seeking more control over, and intrusion into our lives.'*[44]

So be SAFE!

We'll be watching.

And have a nice day now ☠

---

[44] http://www.house.gov/paul/tst/tst2004/tst080904.htm

- 81 -

Drink Two Litres of Water a Day

'I never drink water because of the disgusting things fish do in it.' - **W C Fields**

The human body is a bio-electrical machine that requires a quart of water a day for every 50 lbs of body-weight.[45] The blood alone is made up of a large percentage of watery serum. The lymph fluids, which transport waste and nutrients comprising four times the volume of blood in the body, are made from the water we consume. Every cell that makes us who we are literally owes its life to an adequate supply of fresh, clean water. When the body does not receive a reliable supply of water, it has to ration what is available and cut back on certain functions to make it go around. Essential systems like the brain are prioritised while others are cut back until the brain has decided a reliable source of water has been garnered.

Here's the rub. Most citizens have become chronically and dangerously dehydrated (especially the young and elderly), since we decided water was too bland to drink in favour of tea, coffee, beer, wine, addictive sodas, flavoured water and other chemical-laced alternatives. A disastrous and dangerous move for society's health, to be sure - further compounded by the fact that most doctors today cannot readily identify the many water-deficient diseases and associated pains. Thus the underlying dehydration process continues while drugs are prescribed to switch off the warning signals (symptoms).

---

[45] **Batmanghelidj, F**, *Your Body's Many Cries for Water*, Tagman Press, 2000

World-renowned water expert Dr Fereydoon Batmanghelidj maintains that many common conditions are the body's cries for water, complaints dramatically improved when a consistent, long-term intake of fresh water is introduced. Dr Batman's best-selling book, *Water and Salt, Your Healers From Within,* has helped thousands quash long-term health problems effortlessly and inexpensively.[46] He writes:

'The report of my having successfully treated with water more than three thousand people with symptoms and clinical signs of peptic ulcer disease was published in the Journal of Clinical Gastroenterology in June 1983. I came away from that experience with the understanding that the people I treated were thirsty, and I uncovered the phenomenon that 'pain' in the body indicates thirst, even though the condition is classified as a disease.'[47]

Water is used by the body for digestion, detoxifying cells, watering the lungs, lubricating joints, keeping the body alkalised and a host of cleaning duties. Many symptoms arise out of the body's inability to neutralise or rid itself of acid, a common enough complaint given the number of antacids sold around the world each day. And the dangerous misconception that fuels it?

'I drink coffee, tea, diet sodas, beer and a host of other liquids. They contain water, don't they?'

Many of today's designer drinks are diuretic in their effect (water-expelling) because their mostly acidic compositions require the body to give up water in order to eliminate their harmful residues. Sodas especially are to be avoided since they require

---

46 Ibid.

47 **Batmanghelidj, F**, *Water Cures, Drugs Kill*, Tagman Press, 2003, p. 5

large amounts of body-water to neutralise the phosphoric acid component (2.8 pH) and carbon dioxide (the fizz, which is acidic). Cells that started off healthy and 'plum-like' shrivel to prunes as water, the stuff of life, is progressively denied them. The sick in our hospitals are fed the sodas, tea and coffee they ask for in woeful ignorance of the damage wrought to their micro cell-world within.

Your Body and Dehydration

Batmanghelidj's extraordinary work should rightly be considered by a mainstream medical community ever fixated on the drug cure:

Brain function: The brain comprises 2% of the body's total weight, yet receives 15-20% of the blood supply, mostly comprised of water. Dehydration will affect cognitive ability drastically, and, through histamine's action, can create depressive states (many anti-depressant medications are anti-histamines).

Bone function: Bones require plentiful supplies of water. 75% of the weight of the upper body, for instance, is supported by the water core contained in the fifth lumbar disc, the remaining 25% by muscle fibres around the spine.[48]

Nerve function: Microstreams exist along the length of nerves, which transport nutrients and conduct energy along microtubules to the synapses to transmit messages. Dehydration disrupts proper nerve function, resulting in the sensation of pain.

Hydrolysis: Far from being an inert solvent, water is intricately involved in the body's water-dependent chemical reactions. Lack of water means incomplete or faulty metabolic processes, with obvious implications for losing health. Proteins and

---

[48] Ibid.

enzymes do not function as well in acidic solutions of higher viscosity (stickiness) when the body is dehydrated.

Cellular energy: As water is drawn through the cell membrane, its osmotic flow generates a voltage gradient which can be used in the manufacture of ATP and GTP energy. Dehydration will affect the proper functioning of cells, even kill them.

Histamine: This neurotransmitter activates systems which encourage water intake when dehydration is detected. Functions in the body which consume large quantities of water are cut back, namely the bronchial tubes constricted to cut down on water use in the lungs; increased peristalsis in the bowels to wring more water out of faecal material, and so on. Other signs of histamine's activity, namely allergies, asthma, depression and chronic pains, are interpreted by the physician as 'disease' and treated with steroids, anti-histamines, painkillers (analgesics), etc. Thus the signals of thirst are turned off but the dehydration state continues unabated.

Dyspepsia (heartburn/reflux): Over time, this can lead to ulceration and even cancer. Dr Batmanghelidj recommends that these conditions - also gastritis and duodenitis - be treated with water alone as they are one of the body's major thirst signals. Arrested in his native Iran by the Revolutionary Council during the troubles of the late 1970's, Dr B was confined to Evin prison, Tehran, during which time he successfully treated *with water alone* over three thousand people complaining of dyspeptic pain and associated symptoms.

Digestion: Requires plentiful supplies of water. The stomach relies on mucus lining the walls to shield it from the effects of the stomach's hydrochloric acid. A bicarbonate solution is produced from the cells in the lining which neutralises any acid attempting to break through the mucus. Water is needed to maintain this effective defence system. Too little water, and the mucus barrier is ineffectual, the acid will penetrate and lead to pain. Ideally, water should be consumed half an hour before a meal, in time to anticipate the production of digestive acid from glands in the stomach wall.

Ulcers: Often located at the valve between the stomach and duodenum. Said to be caused by curved bacteria known as helicobacters. Many people have helicobacters in their small intestine, yet not all of them suffer ulcers. Histamine-producing nerves are located at this site, which monitor the through-put of acidic food chyme from the stomach into the intestine. Dr Batman reports histamine has growth-hormone effects on these micro-organisms, resulting in small intestine bacterial overgrowths (SIBOs). An adequate regime of water intake, he maintains, will allow all the functions relating to digestion to normalise. Prolonged water intake should be considered before more drastic drug treatments are entered into.

Summary

You can go without food for a month, but seven days without water and you're all done. Your body cries out for it, your blood is made up of it, nerves, heart, lungs, bowels and brain don't function without it, yet we answer the body's thirst signals with tea, coffee, Fanta, Diet Coke, Red Bull and drugs. Hardly any wonder most western nations have a pub/bar culture to deal with the ravening thirst of their citizens.

Many illnesses respond well to adequate hydration. Mental performance is enhanced. Limbs operate. Blood thinned. Pain banished. Bowels happy. Skin lustrous and clear. Toxins flushed away. Water, the stuff for life. *Are you getting enough?*

- Drink two litres of water a day
- Avoid fluoridated water![49]
- Don't drink tap water unless filtered by reverse osmosis or better [50]
- Bottled water is OK, if a little old and expensive
- Avoid water served in soft plastic bottles, as these impart oestrus activity
- Eat high-water-content fruits and veggies

See also:
Juice Veggies
You Are What Your Eat
Get In The Raw
Free Up Your Digestive Cycles
Choose the Right Doctor
Limit Caffeine, Alcohol and Carbonated Drinks
Eat Greens
Do A Bowel Cleanse

Books available from www.credence.org:
Water, The Stuff of Life
Water and Salt, Your Healers From Within

---

[49] Day, Phillip *Water, The Stuff of Life,* Credence 2004

[50] For more information, see store at www.credence.org

~ 80 ~
Live in the Present

'If he had his wish, he'd be somewhere else.'

Some of us are not really here at all.

Our body is present but our mind's surfing Daytona.

In most of the hotels I speak at, the staff don't really want to be there, I hear the stories. They hate their job, loathe the boss, detest the hours. Their life will one day get better, they tell me, when they get the new car; get the new job; get a pay rise; get a decent girlfriend; when England wins the World Cup; when Hugh Heffner becomes a monk.

- In the meantime, their most precious resource, time, is being squandered
- They're sucking air in the present, but their minds are somewhere else
- If this is you, goals need to be set
- There is enjoyment and success in *every day*
- Don't live in the past either, the elderly do this a lot
- Those who live in the past have nothing to look forward to in the future

Get inspired about what you can do *now*, with the resources you have. Visit a bookstore and spend an hour seeing what everyone else is up to. Bookstores are great sources of inspiration. If the blandness of your current predicament is causing you vacant looks, turn up your own pain so you'll do something about it.

See also:

Time is Your Most Precious Resource
Set Goals Daily
Think Good Thoughts, Don't Dwell on Evil
Never Retire
Take Four-Week Holiday
Work At Self-Improvement
Own a Good Conscience
Avoid National Media
There is Danger in Excess, Moderation in All Things
Live One Day at a Time
Dare to Dream
Be Inspired
Enjoy Silence

- 79 -
Admit When You're Wrong

'I made a mistake once.' - **Lance Falstaff**

It's a sign of character.

It shows others you recognise your limits.

Which makes you more trustworthy.

- 78 -

Eat Apricot Kernels Every Day

'Like cancer, scurvy was believed to be incurable, then in 1747 it was discovered that it was simply caused by a lack of fresh food. Today, many people believe that eating apricot kernels, a food source rich in a vitamin called Vitamin B17, can protect against, and maybe even help to cure, cancer. 'Add Lib' investigates the controversial claims behind B17 and asks, is it possible that it may be to cancer what vitamin C was to scurvy?' - **Ad Lib magazine**

So begins one of many articles about apricot kernels and what they can do for you. In over twenty years of investigation into what works with cancer and what doesn't, I have found dietary changes, vitamin B17 and a less stressful lifestyle come to the fore in successes.

So what's the deal? Apricot kernels are a favourite of a number of agrarian peoples such as the Hunzas, Abkhasians and Karakorum, who have no record of cancer in their isolated states and are famous for long lifespans. Other peoples around the world consume different sources of a nutrient that has come to be known as Vitamin B17 and have similar success.[51] According to scientists who have studied and published, B17 must work in conjunction with enzymes, vitamins C, A & E to achieve a targeted anti-cancer effect in the body. It cannot, and does not work alone.[52]

Vitamin B17 is a stable, chemically inert and non-toxic molecule when taken as food or as a refined pharmaceutical in appropriate

---

[51] **Day, Phillip** *Health Wars,* op. cit.

[52] **Day, Phillip** *B17 Metabolic Therapy, A Technical Manual,* Credence, 2004

quantities (Laetrile and amygdalin are two examples). Scientists discovered the compound reacts to the enzyme beta-glucosidase, located in abnormal amounts at the site of cancerous tumours. In this reaction, beta-glucosidase manufactures two potent poisons, hydrogen cyanide and benzaldehyde (a painkiller), stabilised with two molecules of glucose. These two poisons, produced in minute quantities at the cancer cell site, combine synergistically to kill the cell as part of Vitamin B17's unique, selective toxicity.

So state scientists studying B17, who were aware that indigenous peoples consuming nitrilosidic foods were not experiencing any harmful side-effects from this reaction. On the contrary, their lives were characterised by abundant good health and longevity. Later they found healthy tissue broke down excess levels of B17 into two nutritious by-products, one of which, sodium thiocyanate, reacts with the precursor hydroxycobalamin in the liver to form another nutrient with the cyanide radical: Vitamin B12 (cyanocobalamin).

Biochemist Ernst T Krebs Jr popularised the use of B17 in the sixties and remarked: *'We hear a great deal about its use in terminal cancer, but the time to start with Vitamin B17 is now before the disease becomes clinical. The time to start is the same with any matter of adequate nutrition and that is right now. You may start now by commencing to eat the seeds of all common fruits that you eat. Apricot and peach seeds contain almost 2 percent of Vitamin B17 by weight. The apple seed, although very small, is equally rich in Vitamin B17 - so are the seeds of prunes, plums, cherries, and nectarines. The only common fruits on the hemisphere that lack nitrilosidic seeds are the citrus fruits. This lack has come about by artificial cultivation, by breeding and hybridization, since the seeds of citrus fruits on the African continent still contain Vitamin B17.'*[53]

Recommendations

- Increase the quantity of nitrilosidic (B17) foods in your diet (see list at the back)
- Officially, by order of UK's Food Standards Agency, you're not supposed to consume more than 2-3 seeds a day or you might die of cyanide poisoning. Unofficially, I have to report the Hunzas don't do that; they sometimes eat dozens a day, harvesting the fruit growing wild in the Himalayan foothills. Nothing's happened to them yet
- I've been consuming 7 g a day for years with nothing but benefits. I started with one or two a day and worked up to the 7 g over a week and a half. These days I sprinkle them on my salads and grind them into my veggie juices. People with cancer sometimes take more - 20/40 a day, depending on bodyweight - in addition to cleaning up their diet [54]
- Not all apricot seeds are effective. There are many 'sweet' hybrids on the market. Seeds must have the characteristic bitter taste, indicating the active ingredients are present
- Don't eat seeds whole. May be pulped, grated or crushed or put into veggie juices
- Consumption should be spread throughout the day
- Cancer sufferers should refer to my book, *Cancer: Why We're Still Dying to Know the Truth* for physicians' reports on treating their condition nutritionally (See **Avoid Cancer)**

---

53 Second Annual Cancer Convention, Ambassador Hotel, Los Angeles, 1974

54 **Day, Phillip** *Cancer: Why We're Still Dying to Know the Truth*, Credence 2005

- In a minority of cases, nausea may be experienced when taking apricot kernels. In this event, consumption should be reduced or discontinued
- **Please note:** Some cancer sufferers believe that apricot kernels alone are all that is required to fight cancer. Consultation with a qualified health practitioner familiar with Metabolic Therapy is advised for further information. Apricot kernels are usually part of the nutritional support for those exercising cancer prevention *for life* as well as patients undergoing Phase 1 or Phase 2 Metabolic Therapy.

See also:
You Are What You Eat
Get in the Raw
Avoid Cancer
Choose the Right Doctor
Eat Less But Often
Eat Greens
Juice Veggies
Exercise Prevention

- 77 -
Simplify, Simplify, Simplify

- Consider the rate at which you're living your life
- If speed is the problem, knock holes in your schedule to slow down the hamster wheel
- I was never at anyone's death bed where their last words were: 'Darn, I wish I'd spent more time at the office'
- Simplifying your lifestyle has a beneficial effect on others around you
- Simplicity reduces stress
- There's more time to think
- And more time to consider those things which mean the most to you

See:
Time is Your Most Precious Resource
Set Goals Daily
Lose the Mobile Phone
Take a Four-Week Holiday
Master Yourself: Listen to What Comes Out of Your Mouth

~ 76 ~
Never Retire

'When I was a boy, the Dead Sea was only sick.' - **George Burns**

When productivity ends, so can our will to go on. A gold watch and a pat on the back can be interpreted as the golden boot: *'All right, thank you very much. Make way for the young now.'* You're nothing but a 'human resource', off to the post office and then to the scrap-heap, drawing your pension once a week and scratching down lottery numbers while other people's children squirt you with water pistols.

Lack of goals and a drop in productivity can spell disaster for the recently retired. The sudden change in pace and lack of mental stimulation seem refreshing at first, but can lead to boredom, feelings of worthlessness, chronic depression and Jerry Springer. To compensate, many elderly adopt the habit of living in the past, which tells me they have nothing to look forward to. Far better to stay focused in the here-and-now, remaining active and mentally engaged, not slothful.

Find a job you like or start a business. Set mental tasks. Plan goals. Stay social and relevant. Travel. Make your fondest memories the years in which you have the greatest investment. What do you wish to accomplish by bed-time tonight? (*The scale of achieving does not matter!*)

- Retirement? I'm utterly against it
- Continue producing, you'll have more fun
- The insurance companies have embezzled your pension fund anyway

- Never retire FROM something, always retire TO something
- Now is the time to use your skills to start a new project
- If you are lazy and not working at eighty, GET A JOB
- The extra income will be useful
- In most long-lived cultures, retirement is unknown. Everyone produces, some still fathering sprogs at ninety
- Employ the elderly. Seventy-year-olds know a lot of stuff
- Dream - Plan - Deliver, and I don't mean pizza
- According to the longevity experts, at 65 you are approximately 55% of the way through your lifespan potential!
- Sitting at home does nothing but provoke feelings of worthlessness (big nocebo), owned up to even by lottery winners, who often face depression or return to work to avoid going loopy
- Why not work for yourself?
- Create! Produce! Serve!
- Show someone you're still alive
- Blink!

The definition of success:
Spending your time in your own way

See also:
Time is Your Most Precious Resource
Set Goals Daily
Live in the Present
See The World and Have No Fear
Laugh a Lot

- 75 -

Be Reliable

'Jesus was born on a bank holiday and died on a bank holiday. We can therefore assume that when He returns, it will also be on a bank holiday.' - **P G Johnson**

If you say you're going to do something -

DO IT!

Don't be a flake, others are depending on you.

- 74 -

Reconcile Your Fear of Death

'I don't mind dying. The trouble is, you feel so bloody stiff the following day.' - **George Axlerod**

Dear Phillip, I'm frightened of dying.

Dear Jack, the death-rate is still one per person with a 100% hit-ratio, we're all going to make it. No-one gets out of this gig alive.

Dear Phillip, WHAT CAN I DO?

Dear Jack, GET A LIFE!!!

Fear of their own mortality strikes many, I get the letters. This fear is compounded by media's relentless treatment of death as mankind's last great taboo, which hardly helps. So how do you reconcile your fear of death when you know there is a day appointed in the future for your demise?

Reconciling *the purpose of your existence* is the fundamental place to start. What do you think is the point of it all? Why do you think you here? Notice the importance of belief systems, which propel motivation.

My Famous Motivation Scale (0-10)

0 - I am dead. No longer breathing. I am beyond human help.

1-4 - I suffer from abject depression. I cannot take action. I am listless, suicidal, physically unfit/unwell. No one understands me. The world is going to hell in a hand-basket. I am often medicated and sedated. I have bad dreams. I have to take drugs to maintain any semblance of normality. Why do I even bother breathing? My parents/wife/husband do not understand me. I eat junk food and watch disturbing TV. I have no belief in any future existence beyond my own life. I don't know where I fit in. I am tormented and just want the pain to end. I...er... oh, it doesn't matter.

5 - My existence and life bore me. I cannot be bothered with most activities beyond doing those things necessary to my survival. I am apathetic. I walk around looking at others wondering what planet they're from. I hate my boss, dislike my job, am unproductive and constantly moan. I'm permanently broke. I don't often travel and never enjoy going abroad. Everyone's a hypocrite, especially those who think they have the answer to what ails me. What's the point in looking after yourself? No one gets out alive anyway. Yes, I use cigarettes, alcohol and drugs, *do you have a problem with that?* OK, so I'm tetchy and hostile - it's how you have to be to get by. Yes, I'm frustrated. I hate people who have more than I do. Do I care about my existence? *Whatever.*

6-9 - OK. All this makes sense to me. Show me what to do and I'll get busy. Life's good. I am curious and interested about things. I like to research and discover new ideas. People say I am pleasant to be around. I am productive. I like helping others. Yes, I have rainy days and trials in my life, but that's the human condition. I am optimistic, confident, financially solvent, and have a great relationship. What happens when I die? Not really sure, but I'm trusting in something good. If I get discouraged or depressed, I soon pull myself out of it. I am physically fit and like to take care of myself.

10 - I am on a mission. I can honestly say I am the happiest now that I have ever been. It doesn't get better than this. I understand something of the world and my place in it. I have a balanced appreciation for others with whom I share this planet. I know I am only on Earth a short while, so I am going to act and live in a way that reflects credit upon my existence. I know there are bad things happening in the world but I am determined to keep positive, strive for excellence, and have no regrets. I am passing through to some ultimate destination. I cannot wait to get there and experience my destiny.

Which one applies to you?

The Four BIG Questions

Life's experiences will lead you to develop a belief system, which will give you a context for why you're here in the first place. At some stage, everyone asks themselves the four big questions:

- Who am I?
- Where did I come from?
- What am I doing here?
- Where am I going when this life is over?

Motivational trainer and businessman Brian Tracy believes: *'To be truly happy, you need a clear sense of direction. You need a commitment to something bigger and more important than yourself. You need to feel that your life stands for something, that you are somehow making a valuable contribution to your world.'*[55]

Much misery comes from not possessing the above. Hopelessness sets in that we might have landed in some twilight zone wherein our participation is demanded for no appreciable payback. And anyway, if evolution's right and we're all here by

---

55 Tracy, Brian, *Maximum Achievement*, Simon & Schuster, New York: 1993, p.29

blind, random chance, what the hell's the point? What if the Hokey Cokey really is what it's all about? [56]

There are only two choices:

- You're here by blind, random chance
- Or there's a design for your life

I have the feeling life is a learning process. And I have my own ideas on who might be doing the teaching, which I came to through the process of trying to comprehend precisely why it was I was expending so much effort on living. I came to believe the purpose of life is to survive, grow and learn. To do this, we must take control over our decision-making processes and destiny. And I believe life's experiences direct us to a greater understanding of the bigger questions of who we might be, what the purpose is of it all, and what might be waiting when this life is over. Developing a belief system will give you a context for why you're here and go a long way towards reconciling any fear you have over death. The end of a day is expected, even welcomed. If goals have been met and all is as it should be, what harm in goodnight?

See also:
You're Never Too Old to Change
The Sky Rarely Falls In
Think Good Thoughts, Don't Dwell on Evil
Live in the Present
Never Retire
Turn Off the TV

---

[56] There are all sorts of problems with the theory of evolution, taught in most schools today as *fact*. For more science info, see **Sodera, Vij** *One Small Speck to Man*, available through www.credence.org

Don't Lose Your Joy
Live One Day at a Time
Dare to Dream
Be Thankful
Have a Point to it All

- 73 -

Breathe Clean Air

'Breathe, Mavis! Heavens, we don't want to bury you with that look on your face!' - **Bob Sopwith**

A daily routine of 60-90 minutes outside in suitable surroundings will assist the body in ridding itself of carbon dioxide (acid) and oxygenate tissues with fresh air. Three bouts of vigorous exercise a week are recommended (be safe!). This is ideally combined with pet-walking or other outdoor activity to give rein to the body's requirements for movement and Vitamin D.

Don't miss these steps!

See also:
Exercise – Walk 10,000 Steps a Day
Get a Hobby
Get a Pet
Drink Two Litres of Water a Day
Never Retire
Work at Self-Improvement
Create Overwhelming Optimistic Experiences
Climb Stairs Whenever You Can
Enjoy Silence
Be Disciplined

- 72 -

Strive for Excellence

'Assassins!' -

Italian conductor, Arturo Toscanini, to his orchestra

In today's powder-puff society, excellence is sneered at as élitist and unwholesome. What poppycock. I say go for it and don't worry about causing someone else a 'mental illness'. If you have a skill, use it!

- Develop a healthy, competitive spirit
- Be a gracious winner
- Be an even more gracious loser
- Compete against those who are better than you are, it's the fastest way to improve
- Practise often
- Accept failure as an inevitable component of progress
- Celebrate success
- Never, never, *NEVER* give up!

See also:
Set Goals Daily
Be an Overcomer
Don't Lose Your Joy
Work at Self-Improvement
There is Danger in Excess, Moderation in All Things
Experience Success
Be Disciplined
Be Inspired
Dare to Dream
Avoid Dreamkillers

- 71 -
How's Your Blood Sugar?

Do you suffer from a sugar addiction, trembling, anxiety, overweight, fatigue, wobbly if hungry, confusion, irritability, palpitations, blurred vision, cold hands and feet, low blood pressure, blackouts, angry outbursts, rambling speech, violence, peeing a little often, depression, inappropriate or strange behaviour, forgetfulness, road rage, and an inability to concentrate?

Chances are, you're one of the millions who suffer from blood sugar abnormalities because of your diet and lifestyle.

The brain runs on glucose, claiming up to 30% of the body's production of this essential sugar. 'Blood sugar' levels are vital to the correct functioning of both brain and body in the right amounts and at the right rate. When this delicate balance is disrupted, hypoglycaemia (low blood sugar) or hyperglycaemia (high blood sugar) result, throwing you into turmoil. It's estimated 1 in 4 of us may be suffering from some form of glucose intolerance, manifesting in the problems above as well as insulin resistance and its end-game, diabetes mellitus, type 2.

Tea, coffee, sucrose, chocolate, junk food, cigarettes and other 'mood enhancers' are constantly available in mental institutions. Not good. These stimulate the production of adrenalin and fool the body into releasing glucose from the liver (glycogen) before it is required. Blood sugar levels soar. Frequent intakes of these foods cause the pancreas to over-produce insulin, the hormone responsible for transporting glucose into the cells.

Excess amounts of insulin then cause blood sugar levels abruptly to dive. Symptoms of glucose intolerance set in and a vicious cycle is created as more sugar is craved to relieve the symptoms. Chaotic fluctuations of high and low blood sugar will end you up with an exhausted pancreas and adrenal glands, not to mention the accompanying physical and mental woes described earlier.

All this is controllable with diet and exercise. Remember: bread, pasta, doughnuts, potatoes, chips (fries), rolls, breakfast cereals, rice (no matter how righteous) and all grains *break down into glucose in the body.* If this energy is not burnt off, your brain will stash it where you hang your six-guns (*fat* never made you fat!). Since most don't exercise but still hog down these foods, they end up with problems with blood sugar, critters (Candida), and get cranky, growly and wobbly when you ask them to pass the mustard. If that's you, try the following:

- **COMMENCE THE *FOOD FOR THOUGHT* LIFESTYLE REGIMEN (**at the back of the book), ensuring you cut out junk foods, especially sodas and soft drinks, sucrose, refined high-glycaemic carbohydrates such as ALL GRAINS AND POTATOES
- Eat small meals often to even out blood sugar
- Give up the foods and beverages listed in the **Foods to Avoid** section, especially alcoholic drinks, and ESPECIALLY BEERS AND LAGERS
- If fungi and yeasts have become a problem, switch to the **ANTI-*CANDIDA* LIFESTYLE REGIMEN** (See section on ***Candidiasis*** in *ABC's of Disease*)
- **VITAL:** Increase water intake to four pints (2 litres) per day
- **VITAL:** Work up to regular, vigorous exercise (at least one hour per day, 3-4 times per week, and I don't mean dragging

Toto round the cricket pitch). Consult a doctor if you have to (be safe ☺)

- **COMMENCE THE BASIC SUPPLEMENT PROGRAM**, and **ANTI-*CANDIDA*/FUNGAL SUPPLEMENTATION** if appropriate. Add to that:
- Zinc gluconate, 25 mg, twice per day
- Chromium picolinate, 200 mcg per day, taken every other day, two weeks on, two weeks off.
- Manganese, 10 mg, twice per day

Don't say I don't care about you.

Avoid handling weapons during treatment.

- 70 -
See the World and Have No Fear

'I'm not taking my wife with me to Paris because you don't take a sausage roll to a banquet.' - **Winston Churchill**

Part of life's rich tapestry is travel and adventure. Memories of Egypt or Australia will last a lifetime and so will the photos. Sadly, for the last forty years since terrorism has been widely reported, many have adopted a siege mentality and aren't going anywhere, not even for family. Fear of flying. Fear of bombs. Fear of the fear itself.

As part of my job, I am very fortunate to travel widely. And the world I see is nowhere close to the world of CNN and the BBC. I find stunning vistas, friendly people going about their daily business, different cultures, exotic animals, new experiences and no regrets. What I don't see are all the muggings, rapes, murders, terrorism and global warming compressed into those half-hour bulletins that give everyone the screaming heebie-jeebies and keep them indoors with the Bovril.

Steer clear of the media! See the world and have no fear. Most of us are stressed and could use a break. We are fortunate that never in the history of mankind since the Vikings has overtaking another's country been more satisfying to the spirit. It will definitely change your life, ask George Bush.

Then again, perhaps you'll learn more about other cultures experiencing them personally rather than down a bomb-site from 35,000 feet. Blimey, some of us have even gone off for a trot out there, found somewhere we liked and gone bloody native! On the other hand, if you don't want your life changed and all your joy is 32, Bettany Gardens, London SW, you'll appreciate it a lot more if you spend a little time away, and I don't mean down the pub.

Exercise prudence. Basra might not be the best spot to take Aunt Ruby right now, though I understand Beirut has regained its former reputation as a sizzling hotspot and is back in the travel mags. *What? No it isn't?* Adventures mend relationships, break them, get you thinking philosophically about your place in life, stir up your passions. One of my favourite things to do is go somewhere to finish writing a book. I finished *The Mind Game* in Sorrento, Italy, and had an unforgettable few days exploring Pompeii, the Roman town buried under volcanic ash in 70AD. *The Little Book of Attitude* was completed looking out the window of a fortified French farmhouse near Falaise, walls peppered with bullet holes from Canadian troops storming the Nazi headquarters. *Cancer...* was written in California and Texas. *Health Wars* was started in the Seychelles, written on tour in America and Canada, and completed on the shores of New Zealand's Lake Taupo with a snow-capped Mount Ruapehu in the distance.

- It's a beautiful world out there
- Made for you
- Waiting for you
- And you can take double the luggage if you go via LA

See also:
Take a Four-Week Holiday
Be Inspired

~ 69 ~
Eat Half a Pineapple a Day

'The origin of many anti-cancer drugs can be found in nature.' - **Dr Julie Sharp**

No.1 - Pineapples are good for you

No.2 - they contain the enzyme bromelain

No.3 - Nutritive elements in pineapple have been the subject of studies examining their anti-cancer and anti-inflammatory effects, as well as immune-regulating properties.

Ernst Krebs Jr and his father, Ernst Krebs Sr. MD, (he of the 'Krebs Cycle') are credited with concentrating their studies on the knowledge and use of enzymes, including bromelain, chymotrypsin, trypsin and papain, in the treatment of cancer. Both Krebs and his father are widely recognised today as the 'fathers' of vitamin B17 (amygdalin, Laetrile) in its role in treating cancer, though the substance was in use as a medicinal aid much earlier.[57]

Today, of course, the medical establishment does its best to dissuade you from suggesting food does much else other than keep you alive, certainly not fixing you if you're sick! Indeed, as with those vitamin discoveries before it, B17 produced quite a controversy in the sixties, which rolling barrage of acrimony continues to this day. As ever, the orthodoxy routinely labels most food cures quackery, in spite of the evidence.

---

[57] **Day, Phillip** *B17 Metabolic Therapy Manual,* op. cit.

Anyway, pineapples and bromelain: Dr Harold Manner and his team of graduate students at Loyola University, Chicago were studying the effects of Vitamin B17 on cancer when combined with enzymes and Vitamins A and E in their emulsified form. Further south in Mexico, Dr Ernesto Contreras, one of that country's most respected doctors, was fielding similar research. Manner and Contreras contended that B17 and associated vitamins could not produce noticeable anti-cancer results without the cancer 'shell' (protein coating) first being attacked and stripped by enzymes. The natural action of pancreatin, trypsin, papain and bromelain does just that - weaken and digest the protein coating of trophoblast (cancer) cells, allowing the body's immune system lymphocytes to destroy them.[58] Krebs Jr stated:

'Pancreatic and vegetable enzymes are part of the supportive theory [in cancer]. *You have the papaya melons as the source of the enzyme papain and pineapple as a source of the enzyme bromelain. The demasking effect of these enzymes against the pericellular layer of the malignant cell is something very concrete in the immunology of cancer. Now I prefer, rather than advising the use of bromelain or papaya tablets, that the individual seeking these enzymes gets them directly from the fresh, ripe pineapple and papaya fruit. As much as half a pineapple a day should be ingested.*

'This is the way to go. You have nothing to lose by eating fresh pineapple and papaya melons. Nothing to lose by eating millet, the seeds of all the common fruits and whole, fresh foods.'[59]

---

[58] **Manner, Harold** *The Death of Cancer*, Metabolic Research Foundation, 1989
[59] Second Annual Cancer Convention, Ambassador Hotel, Los Angeles, 1974

TWO MOLECULES ISOLATED FROM AN EXTRACT OF CRUSHED PINEAPPLE STEMS HAVE SHOWN PROMISE IN FIGHTING CANCER GROWTH.

So stated the BBC on 22nd July 2005. The report goes on to state: *'...The extract studied by the scientists, bromelain, is a rich source of enzymes and is widely used as a meat tenderiser, to clarify beer and tan leather hides.*

The [Queensland Institute of Medical Research] *discovered the extract also had pharmacological properties and could activate specific immune cells while simultaneously blocking the immune function of other cells.*

Lead researcher Dr Tracey Mynott said: 'We suspected that different components of the crude mixture might be responsible for bromelain's biological effects.

'In searching for these components, we discovered the CCS and CCZ proteins and found that they could block growth of a broad range of tumour cells, including breast, lung, colon, ovarian and melanoma.'

The report unhelpfully concludes: *'It is hoped the research... could lead to new anti-cancer drugs.'*

What tosh. As Krebs says, eat the pineapple. On top of which, you also have the benefit of consuming fruit before noon on an empty stomach to assist the body in shedding weight and toxins during elimination. Pineapples are rich in vitamins, minerals, amino acids, enzymes - all in all, a right royal addition to the morning arsenal to promote great health and healing.

See also:

Free Up Your Digestive Cycles
Avoid Cancer
You Are What You Eat
Get in the Raw
Exercise Prevention

~ 68 ~

Laugh a Lot!

'Teenagers, are you tired of being harassed by your stupid parents? Act now. Move out, get a job, and pay your own bills – while you still know everything.'

– **John Hinde**

Laughter relieves stress, makes you pull faces, and gets you taking life a little less seriously. Let's face it, laughing's pretty funny, though too much of it and they'll think there's something wrong with you. Look at Jim Carrey.

The Washington Post reports: *'A hearty laugh a day may keep the doctor away, say the findings of a unique study. Whereas previous studies have examined how negative emotions can adversely affect our health, this study took a new spin - they measured the affect of watching a funny movie on the ability of heart blood vessels to expand. And they found some surprising results - laughing increased blood flow as much as a 15- to 30-minute workout.*

The ability of blood vessels to expand is known as vasodilation. Poor vasodilation means that passageways may be blocked and blood flow may be cut off. The result is an increased risk of heart attacks and strokes. In the study, 20 healthy men and women watched clips of two movies - a violent battle scene from "Saving Private Ryan" or a humorous scene from a comedy such as "Kingpin." Each participant's vasodilation was measured prior to the movie and again afterward.

The results were "dramatic." Of the 20 participants who saw the stressful film, 14 had significantly reduced blood flow. However, after watching the funny film, 19 of the 20 volunteers had significantly increased blood flow. Specifically:

- *Blood flow decreased by about 35 percent after experiencing stress*
- *Blood flow increased by 22 percent after laughing, which is equivalent to what happens after a 15- to 30-minute workout.*[60]

Paul J Rosch MD, president of the American Institute of Stress, agrees: *'In one study of 2,500 senior citizens who were followed for six years, those who scored high on a happiness quiz had much fewer strokes than those at the bottom of the scale. In another study of more than 200 middle-aged healthy London civil service employees, those who reported feeling happy almost every day, whether while at work or on weekends, were significantly healthier and had lower heart rates than others who were not as consistently jolly and gleeful.*

After adjusting for age, smoking, weight and other possible influences, it was found that people in the top fifth for daily happiness scores had cortisol levels 32 percent lower than those in the bottom quintile. Happiness was also linked to a lower average heart rate in men. While the majority showed some rise in fibrinogen following the mental stress test, this was far greater for the least happy group compared to those at the other end of the scale.

---

60 *Washington Post,* 14th March 2005

...benefits of laughing reported by this and other groups here and abroad include:

- *Relaxation and reduction in muscle tension*
- *Lowered production of stress hormones*
- *Improved immune system function*
- *Reduction in blood pressure*
- *Clearing the lungs by dislodging mucous plugs*
- *Increasing the production of salivary immunoglobulin A, which defends against infectious organisms that enter through the respiratory tract*
- *Aerobic effects that increased the body's ability to utilize oxygen*
- *A rapid ability to disregard aches and pains or to perceive them as less severe*[61]

So get chortling.

See also:
You're Never Too Old to Change
Think Good Thoughts, Don't Dwell on Evil
Avoid Psychiatrists
Don't Lose Your Joy
Be in Love
Create Overwhelming Optimistic Experiences
Reward Yourself
Read a Good Book
Enjoy Music

---

[61] *Health and Stress,* November 2005 - www.stress.org

~ 67 ~
Deal With Chronic Issues

'The proliferation of massage establishments in London in the last few years appears to indicate a dramatic increase in muscular disorders among the male population.' - **Evelyn Waugh**

Do you have a problem that refuses to clear up? Best get it sorted out, some become more serious later. In my compendium, *The ABC's of Disease,* I cover most of the physical and mental issues, so the chances are yours will be among them.[62] Here's a combined list of angles to get a feel for what to look for:

- Chronic financial problems
- Out of breath for no reason
- Toenail fungus/thrush/jock itch/yeast problems
- Eczema/psoriasis/rashes
- Blood sugar imbalance
- Unforgiveness
- Dizziness
- Feelings of depression/doom/suicide
- Addictions
- Peeing problems (little and often)
- Miscellaneous pains and lumps
- Digestion problems
- Reflux (heartburn)
- Back pain

Chronic conditions play on the mind. Many are simply lifestyle and diet issues that *will* clear up if you make better choices.

---

[62] **Day, Phillip** *The ABC's of Disease,* op. cit.

~ 66 ~
Take a Four-Week Holiday

'One in three British workers fail to take their full annual holiday entitlement, a survey has shown. Instead, they put in 36 million hours of free overtime, giving bosses almost £1 billion in unpaid work every year -'

We must be barking mad. And if we do go on holiday -

The survey of nearly 6,000 workers by the Chartered Management Institute found nearly half stay in contact with their employer while they are away.' - Daily Mail, 15th June 2005

No! No! No! No! No!

Behavioural patterns are formed over a 15- to 30-day period through repetition and a state of emotional excitement (what I term the Pavlov Principle). They overwrite over the same period. Few of us take four-week holidays, which is why we still have bats in the belfry. Pavlov's Principle relies on location, repetition and the 30-day conditioning period, so clearing off somewhere nice for a break makes all the sense in the world, especially if we go to play. *For four weeks.*

Take those who relax you. Leave the kids at home if necessary (straight-jackets are for this). Go forth and frivolate, you've earned it. The first ten days of your four-week re-adjustment are usually spent cussing out Spanish waiters and being generally beastly as the mental puke gushes out. After that, serenity and bliss usually prevail or your travel agent will give you your money back.

- Now go and play
- *Do not take the laptop or anything connected with work*
- Do not *ever* phone work
- Do not *ever* tell your boss where he can reach you
- Do not phone home and get stressed
- Tell family to contact you only in an extreme emergency, otherwise *sayanara,* you'll buy them a tee-shirt
- In fact, **Lose the Mobile Phone**
- Eat raw, living, organic whole-foods
- Exercise (more play)
- Behave inappropriately (even more play). It's a holiday
- *Don't* burn. *Do* get some sun
- Dreaming comes easier with a magenta sunset and a Mai-Tai. These are the times of refreshing and inspiration. Get refreshed, sunshine.

DIRE WARNING: THOSE WHO DON'T TAKE HOLIDAYS ARE TREASURING UP FOR THEMSELVES PROBLEMS FOR THE FUTURE. YOU SELF-EMPLOYED ARE THE WORST FOR THIS!

IN FACT...

~ 65 ~
Listen to What Comes Out of Your Mouth

It's a good indication of when to take the four-week holiday

He was shouting in a sort of Franglais, 'I will frappez votre teeth so far down votre gorge, you'll be able to manger avec your derrière.' - **Victor Lewis-Smith**

Master yourself.

Stay in control.

Operate efficiently.

When you start losing it, pop down to Dial-a-Flight. It's time to get out of Dodge.

Swearing and other B******s

Did you know US President Andrew Jackson's parrot had to be removed from his funeral because it was swearing? Some have a penchant for it, which they can't shake. The pattern has been installed subconsciously through repetition and can be extirpated the same way. Swearing, annoying speech ticks (er, umm, huh? We're off parrots now) and other verbal garbage are patterning addictions (*see* **Get Rid of Addictions**). It'll take a bit of work, then again, how badly do you want to clean up your beak?

A holiday is a good time to work on this, since you are out of your regular environment, temporarily free of associated patterning, and have four weeks to set things straight. Give peace a chance!

See also:

Time is Your Most Precious Resource
Exercise- Walk 10,000 Steps a Day
Think Good Thoughts, Don't Dwell on Evil
See the World and Have No Fear
Laugh a Lot
Admit When You're Wrong
Work at Self-Improvement
Create Overwhelming Optimistic Experiences
Manage Your Anger
Own a Good Conscience
Don't Break the Law
Enjoy Silence
Take Responsibility For Your Actions
Be Disciplined
Be Thankful
Help Others

~ 64 ~

Turn Off the TV

'In a mere half-century, films have gone from silent to unspeakable.' - **Doug Larson**

- TV squanders your most precious resource - time.
- Studies show fast food 'restaurants' and eating in front of the TV are the major contributors to childhood obesity, especially when the junk food they're eating is advertised on TV [63]
- TV is a major source of Pavlov programming
- TV educates kids the wrong way
- Jonathan Ross is always on it

Clearly I'll have an uphill battle getting everyone to switch off the idiot box. Actually that is not my intention, since television brings pleasure to millions and, I believe, has an educative and entertainment part to play in modern culture. Then again like all good ideas, TV has inevitably been abused and taken beyond the pale. Dr Joseph Mercola comments:

'It is very important to keep a handle on this aspect of your life. I am absolutely convinced that television watching is a major determinant of our health problems. It is just too addictive for most of us, especially with the advent of cable and dozens of channels to chose from. It is so easy to get trapped into watching more than you had planned on watching.

[63] Center for Science in the Public Interest, 24th February 2004; The Kaiser Foundation, February 2004

Watching TV will take away from not only your exercise time, but reading and relationship time. I suspect putting strict limits on your watching will be helpful. I try to keep my time to three hours per week or less. The last two weeks I have been able to keep it down to 30 minutes (largely as a result of the fact that ER is in its re-run mode!).[64]

Furthermore: *'A study by researchers at Johns Hopkins University School of Medicine, along with experts at the CDC and the National Institutes of Health, concludes that a child's weight increases with the number of hours he or she spends watching television each day. These experts are calling a US "epidemic" of childhood obesity. Many US children watch a great deal of television and are inadequately vigorously active.*

The researchers discovered that 20% of US children partake in two or fewer bouts of vigorous activity per week. (Health experts currently recommend at least three periods of strenuous exercise per week). The problem stems from the fact that watching television is a sedentary activity - but it's much more than that. Children are watching TV, many times eating high-calorie/high-fat snack foods, and watching commercials for fast food, all of which may encourage more eating.

The study also showed that 26% of US children watched 4 or more hours of television per day. Experts already label television viewing as the number one leisure-time activity of most school-age children. The study's authors point out that the average high

---

64 www.mercola.com

school graduate will likely spend 15,000 to 18,000 hours in front of a television but only 12,000 hours in school.[65]

Author and researcher Bruce Wiseman writes: *'Outside our windows, the peaceful streets of years past now harbour violence. In some neighbourhoods, gunfire pierces the night. Police helicopters fly overhead, scanning yards and alleys for runaway criminals.*

We worry about our children. Once-quiet schools are now hothouses of drug-trafficking, promiscuity, and vice unimaginable in days gone by. We hear of an ever declining literacy rate, dwindling test scores, and of graduates who can't even find their home city on a map. We wonder how they will ever make it in the adult world.

In our homes, at our jobs, on our television screens, we see that the once-clear line between right and wrong has become grey and hazy. Virtue is held up to ridicule. The honest man is viewed as a fool. Criminal behaviour is now excused under the banner of 'irresistible impulse' and 'diminished capacity'.

Hardly anyone would argue with the statement that something has been eating at the moral fabric for decades now.... No one questions that there is a palpable, destructive force. In the United States, for example, people are at each other's throats over it. Liberals blame it on conservative policies, right-wingers

---

[65] Ibid; *The Journal of the American Medical Association* 1998;279(12):938-942, 959-960

rebuke the left. Many in the religious community have held the entertainment industry accountable.'[66]

In his novel, *1984*, George Orwell writes of his controlled society: *'In the past, no government had the power to keep its citizens under constant surveillance. The invention of print however made it easier to manipulate public opinion - film and radio carried the process even further. With the development of television... private life came to an end. Every citizen could be kept, for twenty-four hours a day, under the eyes of the police with all other channels of communication closed. The possibility of enforcing not only complete obedience to the will of the state, but complete uniformity of opinion on all subjects, now existed for the first time.'*[67]

Desensitising the Public to Violence

Glorying in the gore dulls the senses and perverts the mindset. Apathy and a deep kind of sexual thrill are experienced by the viewer, who watches scenes of social as well as sexual degradation nightly on the television or at the movies. The lasting effect is a dulling of the blade of morality and a quenching of the desire to help others. Author Michael Hoffman:

'I remember Budd Dwyer's televised suicide. The Pennsylvania official prefaced his broadcast TV self-immolation with a quote from one of his associates who told Dwyer that the American people had become too jaded about 'routine' investigations into

---

[66] **Wiseman, Bruce** *Psychiatry - The Ultimate Betrayal*, Freedom Publishing, Los Angeles: 1995, pp.5,6

[67] **Orwell, George** *1984*, NAL/Dutton: 1976, p.206

political corruption on TV's 60 Minutes and 20/20 to care very much about the corruption Dwyer sought to expose.

Mr Dwyer decided that a population so jaded would need a spectacular sacrificial victim to shake it awake from its apathy and therefore shot himself in front of TV cameras at a news conference.

But his televised suicide did no such thing. Instead it became, like virtually everything else that appears on television, a trivialised part of the entertainment videodrome. It merely raised the stakes for the next human life to exceed, in terms of violence and horror and brutalisation, as public fare.' [68]

Bruce Wiseman again: *'As* [my] *book is being written, we took a sampling of subject matter from the week's television schedule:*

- *Beverly Hills 90210: 'Donna and Kelly scour the campus for men to pose for their calendar; Steve learns the fraternity president is gay.'*
- *Babylon 5: 'A Centauri slave seduces Londo for information that could destroy him.'*
- *In the Heat of the Night: 'Bubba races to Atlanta to care for his nephew, who has overdosed on drugs.'*
- *Melrose Place: 'Sydney takes over jailed Lauren's escort business....'* [69]

---

68 **Hoffman, Michael** *Secret Societies and Psychological Warfare,* Wiswell Ruffin House, 1992, p.90

69 Wiseman, Bruce, op. cit. p.22

During the writing of *The Mind Game*, a similar sampling of a week's TV fare in the UK revealed a startling conglomeration you wouldn't believe unless you read it:

- A documentary on live sex acts occurring in Ibiza nightclubs, young female holidaymakers taking part while their admiring mothers look on
- Drunken brawls and gratuitous violence at British and European football matches
- A British father rapes his own daughter, then murders her
- The *Sopranos*, where a troubled Mafiosi visits his sexually alluring psychiatrist in between frank psychotic episodes, during which people die messily
- *Buffy The Vampire Slayer*, featuring demons, ghouls, decapitations and schoolgirls in short skirts and little white socks

PS: I have no idea which ends Channel 4 really serves.

Across the gamut today, we have Big Brother, that celebrity scarecrow Russell Brand, Celebrity Love Island, Graham Norton for the old dears, and of course, the inevitable soaps with their faces contorted in rage, anger and hatred. All that and poker on TV too.

Nice.

~ 63 ~

Avoid Psychiatrists

'I don't believe you can scramble brains and expect to have anything left but scrambled brains.' - **Anonymous American Psychiatrist (1942)**

The 18th and 19th centuries brought with them more than just the technical allure of an industrial revolution. Man himself became restless for a spiritual as well as physical change in the way he regarded himself and his place in the cosmos. New 'sciences' emerged, such as evolution, psychology, psychiatry and the mental health and hygiene movements. Their impacts on our future society were to have far-reaching consequences in the decades following their acceptance by the public at large.

At first glance, most would not even acknowledge the incredible damage psychiatry has wrought on our world, permeating our courts, police, hospitals, movies and TV, our schoolyards, governments, even our homes, *and all for the ill.* In fact you may conclude mankind itself must be going insane when we are told repeatedly at no other time in history has society been so 'mentally ill'. Our nations' governments, schools and courts appreciate this, which is why they are veritably a-swarm with armies of legislators, administrators and battalions of psychologists, psychiatrists and mental health experts to cope with the burgeoning workload. One could expect, with such an impressive arsenal of professional expertise on call, victory itself would be assured. Who would consider in their right mind these forces might conceivably be the very same armies responsible for all the chaos?

Thomas Szasz

...is an interesting individual. He's Professor of Psychiatry Emeritus at the State University of New York at Syracuse and Lifetime Fellow of the American Psychiatric Association. After reaching his profession's pinnacle, Dr Szasz has repeatedly denounced psychiatry as *'...probably the single most destructive force that has affected American society within the last fifty years.'* An author of 23 books, including *The Myth of Mental Illness*, described by *Science* magazine as *'bold and often brilliant'*, the Hungarian-born specialist has covered every type of abuse carried out by his profession. As a scientist, Szasz pronounces psychiatry guilty, not only of gross abuses of power and human rights over its patients, nor also of the far-reaching, deleterious effects its philosophies have wrought throughout the world, but of having no cures and no science.[70]

'Psychiatry is a part of the general liberal ethos,' he states. *'...Everybody is a victim, everybody has special rights, no responsibilities. This psychiatric view has so completely infiltrated* [global thinking], *people don't even think of it as psychiatry.'*[71]

The Mind Game Mission

In *The Mind Game,* I trace the origins of psychiatry, this 'science of the mind', and lay bare the unsettling history of this Trojan Horse that has been wheeled into our midst:

---

[70] Citizen's Commission on Human Rights short film *Psychiatry: No Cures, No Science*, viewable at www.cchr.org

[71] CCHR interview with Dr Thomas Szasz, 17th September 1993

- There are no scientific tests in psychiatry to diagnose 'mental illness'[72]
- Psychiatrists admit they don't cure people[73]
- Some of the worst slaughters in recent history have been committed by those with deeply-held psychiatric beliefs
- Psychiatry invents diseases and sells them to the public to great profit
- Citizens are stigmatised by being given a 'mental illness' label
- Hundreds of thousands are incarcerated in institutions around the world on the strength of unscientific diagnoses
- *Electroshock therapy?*
- *Lobotomy???*
- Psychiatry drugs up millions of children and the elderly, not to mention a sizeable chunk of the general population, to change their behaviour, which is not the same as curing 'mental illness'
- Crimes committed by psychiatry outstrip those committed by all other branches of medicine *combined*
- Society has to bear the terrible political and social fall-out of psychiatric thought
- Welcome to the 'human rights' victim culture
- The hamstringing of our police and justice system
- The wrecking of our schools
- School shootings
- Financial rip-offs
- Political correctness

Answers

Without doubt, there are men and women working with all good intention within 'mental health', attempting to make a difference.

---

[72] *Psychiatry: No Science, No Cures*, op. cit.

[73] Ibid.

But you can be sincere, and you can be sincerely wrong. A drastic change of direction is long overdue, with greater understanding of the true causes of emotional disorders.[74] For the millions who wrestle with Alzheimer's, Parkinson's, ADD/ADHD, schizophrenia, anorexia, depression, dyslexia and violence in the home, there *is* some great news which won't be found in a Prozac bottle.

In *The Mind Game,* I examine the real causes of mental illness and show abundant evidence that in most cases, diet, social and lifestyle pressures are to blame. The new science of 'orthomolecular psychiatry', in my view, is the way forward - the science of treating such conditions with the correct ('ortho') molecules. In other words, examining the patient medically first to establish the existence of any physical ailments, then bringing the full arsenal of nutritional medicine and counselling to bear where applicable.

There is a tremendous amount each of us can do to steer clear of problems in the first place. Lifestyle and social pressures, food allergies, toxins, malnutrition and blood sugar problems can all lurk behind strange changes in thought and behaviour.[75] *The Mind Game* was written as a stark light to be shone into the dark places and continues to do its job. Unfortunately, until orthodoxy decides to put patients before profit, we may expect a continuation of the same - the mass drugging of populations to get their brains to forget about what was bothering them to begin with.

I hereby warn the world off psychiatry and its baleful mental health practices.

---

74 Day, Phillip *The Mind Game,* op. cit.

75 Ibid.

Don't go there.

See also:

You Are What You Eat
Free Up Your Digestive Cycles
Choose the Right Doctor
Supplement With Vitamin C
Think Good Thoughts, Don't Dwell on Evil
Drink Two Litres of Water a Day
Laugh a Lot
Take a Four-Week Holiday
Listen to What Comes Out of Your Mouth
Turn Off the TV
Create Overwhelming Optimistic Experiences
Don't Lose Your Joy
Guard Input

~ 62 ~
Don't Be Too Clean!

The September 2002 edition of *Parenting and Pregnancy* includes a report entitled *Dirt May Be Good For Kids*. Part of the account reads as follows:

'Behind the ongoing epidemic of allergy and autoimmune disease there's a surprising culprit: cleanliness. One of the hallmarks of the 20th Century was its war on germs. Kids now live in cleaner homes and suffer fewer infections than their grandparents did. There's irony in this, according to the so-called 'hygiene' theory. It holds that a germ-free childhood warps the immune system. A report in the Sept. 19th issue of The New England Journal of Medicine now offers powerful support for this theory. The researchers carefully vacuumed up dust from the beds of 812 children from rural areas of Austria, Germany, and Switzerland. The dust was measured for a basic component of dirt - the outer cell wall of common bacteria, known to scientists as endotoxin. Also collected were the kids' medical records.

The result: the kids who had the cleanest mattresses had the most hay fever, allergic asthma, and allergic reactions. The kids with the dirtiest beds - and least allergy and asthma - were most likely to live or play on farms. That's no surprise, as earlier studies showed that children raised on farms have fewer allergies and less asthma than rural kids who don't live on farms. Bacteria excreted by cows and other farm animals are the most common source of endotoxin.' [76]

---

[76] 'Dirt May Be Good For Kids', *Pregnancy ands Parenting*, 18th September 2002 at http://content.health.msn.com/content/article/50/40423.htm?pagenumber=1

Health author Steve Ransom comments: *'Are children suffering from the ministrations of over-protective parents? The obsessive or abnormal traits parents attach to dirt, dust, spiders, etc., are 'passed on' to our offspring, leading often to that child experiencing the same bondages, fears and phobias. What a culture shock it is to read that dirt and dust may not be such bad company after all!'*[77]

And they're not. Ransom goes on to introduce us to Jean-François Bach MD, DSc, the director of the INSERM immunology unit at Necker Hospital in Paris. Bach says that as the immune system develops in a child, it needs fine-tuning. Every time it fights a germ, it learns a little more. Eventually, it learns the best way to fight germs and how not to start allergic or autoimmune reactions. Bach warns that overprotection - especially by unneeded antibiotic treatments - can kill off harmless bacteria that have much to teach the immune system.

'I think the first thing is not to worry if a child has a piece of meat falling on the ground and eats it,' says Bach. *'Exposure to some minor infections is not bad. You don't need to sterilise and re-sterilise everything. The main thing is to avoid unnecessary antibiotic therapy.'*[78]

In an article entitled, 'Allergies: Because We're Too Clean', the author states: *'The way we're living is far removed from the day-to-day confrontation with nature the way our ancestors experienced it. We're out of touch with the Earth, too safe and*

---

[77] **Ransom, Steven** *Wake up to Health in the 21st Century*, Credence, 2004

[78] 'Kids With Clean Beds Have More Allergies', *Vaccination News* at www.vaccinationnews.com/DailyNews/September2002/DirtMayGood19.htm

protected. We don't have enough cuts and bruises or dirt under our fingernails.'[79]

Cats and Dogs Prevent Allergies!

Household pets are generally off-limits to anyone with an allergy or asthma. But could pets actually help in the prevention of allergies? A study conducted by doctors in Virginia certainly indicates this. Doctors studied more than 200 children with and without allergies and tested their sensitivity to cat dander and dust mites. They found that children who grew up with cats in the home were less likely to develop allergies.[80]

'Naturally, with all this talk of dust, dirt, cats, dogs and farmyard toxins,' Steven Ransom concludes, *'no-one is suggesting we return to the dirt and squalor that led to so much illness and death witnessed even as late as the early part of last century. There is a sensible middle ground* [emphasis mine!], *wherein an appropriate level of cleanliness may be achieved without slipping into excess.'*[81]

---

79 **Waffle, Van** 'Allergies: Because We're Too Clean', *Living With Nature,* November 19th 2002 at www.suite101.com/article.cfm/5536/96492

80 *Pets and Allergies* at www3.utsouthwestern.edu/library/consumer/petallergy.htm

81 Ransom, Steven, *Wake up to Health,* op. cit.

~ 61 ~
Eat Greens

- Greens contain chlorophyll
- Chlorophyll goes to manufacture haemoglobin, the oxygen-carrying truck in your blood
- Greens are a great source of *fine* calcium (not the coarse junk found in cows' milk)
- Organic greens are rich in minerals, including iron
- Greens are alkalising antioxidants which give protection against cancer
- Greens are rich in amino acids, which make protein
- Greens deliver an impressive enzyme payload when eaten in their raw, unadulterated state
- Greens are the food no-one wants to eat. I've heard them whining and snivelling in the produce section at Sainsburys
- Juice greens and squeeze a lemon into the mix - delicious!

See also:
You Are What You Eat
Get in the Raw
Free Up Your Digestive Cycles
Eat Less But Often
Avoid Cancer
Juice Veggies

Books available through www.credence.org
Food For Thought
The Handbook of Energy Drinks

~ 60 ~

Remove Toxins from Home and Work

'Sure it's going to kill a lot of people, but
they may be dying of something else anyway.'
- Othal Brand, Texas pesticide review board, on chlordane

In *Health Wars* and *Cancer: Why We're Still Dying to Know the Truth*, I devote some time to potential and actual carcinogens to be found in our food, as well as the personal care and household products we use. The problems stem from governments' inability to test and effectively regulate chemicals coming onto the market with the limited budgets they have available. Compounding this are the conflicts of interest existing between chemical manufacturers and government regulatory agencies, making objective adjudication of these drugs and chemicals a near impossibility.[82]

Personal Care and Household Products

Poor regulation, self-regulation and a blizzard of confusing and contrary scientific data have resulted in a large number of chemicals making it into our food and the products we buy with little or no warnings attached. Most people have no idea, for example, what the personal care products they use every day may be doing to them.

In 1990, 38,000 cosmetic injuries were reported in the US that required medical attention.[83] Health concerns are

---

[82] **Day, Phillip** *Cancer: Why We're Still Dying to Know the Truth*, op. cit.

[83] **Steinman, D & Samuel S Epstein** *The Safe Shopper's Bible*, pp. 182-183, ISBN 0020820852; also Consumer Product Safety Commission (CPSC), Product summary report: Washington DC, 1990

continuously being raised over ingredients in shampoos, toothpastes, skin creams and other grooming products. Researchers in Japan, Germany, Switzerland, and the US say many ingredients in personal care products may be related to premature baldness, cataract formation, environmental cancers, contact dermatitis and possible eye damage in young children. The National Institute of Occupational Safety and Health found 884 chemicals available for use in cosmetics had been reported to the US government as toxic substances.[84]

On 10th September 1997, Senator Edward Kennedy of Massachusetts, while discussing an FDA reform bill, stated, *'The cosmetic industry has borrowed a page from the playbook of the tobacco industry by putting profits ahead of public health.'* Kennedy further stated, *'Cosmetics can be dangerous to your health. Yet this greedy industry wants Congress to prevent the American people from learning that truth. Every woman who uses face cream, or hair spray, or lipstick, or shampoo, or mascara, or powder should demand that this arrogant and irresponsible power-play by the industry be rejected. A study by the respected, non-partisan General Accounting Office reported that more than 125 ingredients available for use in cosmetics are suspected of causing cancer. Other cosmetics may cause adverse effects on the nervous system, including convulsions. Still other ingredients are suspected of causing birth defects. A carefully controlled study found that one in sixty users suffered a cosmetic-related injury identified by a physician.'* [85]

---

84 Steinman, D & S Epstein, *Safe Shopper's Bible*, op. cit.

85 Quoted from Senator Kennedy's office on www.senate.gov/~kennedy/statements/970910fda.html

Samuel Epstein MD, a world-renowned authority on the causes and prevention of cancer, was named the 1998 winner of the Right Livelihood Award (also known as the 'Alternative Nobel Prize'). Dr Epstein has devoted the greater part of his life to studying and fighting the causes of cancer. He is Professor of Occupational and Environmental Medicine at the School of Public Health, University of Illinois Medical Center at Chicago, and the chairman of the Cancer Prevention Coalition.

Author of *The Politics of Cancer* and *The Breast Cancer Prevention Program*, Epstein recommends the use of cosmetics and other products that are free from suspected carcinogens. The company he recommends (and so do I) is Neways International. Neways' Convert Your Bathroom pack contains shampoo, conditioner, bath gel, shaving gel, deodorant, toothpaste and mouthwash that are not only free from damaging ingredients, but are of the highest quality. Whether you are undergoing treatment for a condition or are simply interested in exercising disease prevention, stop the cumulative toxic onslaught today:

- Don't poison yourself
- Check every product you are using over the long-haul
- See *Health Wars, Cancer: Why We're...* or *The ABC's of Disease* for more information on which chemicals do what, and which ones to avoid

~ 59 ~
Avoid Cancer

This topic has engaged my interest and investigation for over twenty years and I have published five books on the subject. I became interested in cancer because my relatives kept dying of it. The broad-strokes of cancer and why we fail with it (when we shouldn't) can be summarised as follows:

- The medical establishment has no cure for cancer
- More people today are making a living from cancer than are dying from it[86]
- They have re-defined the word 'survive' to mean you've 'made it' if you're still alive five years after initial treatment
- In fact, more advanced diagnostic techniques have brought time to be able to claim '80% of women are surviving breast cancer' by this rule, when it should be considered whether these women survive the disease at all, whatever the time-frame
- My extensive investigations reveal the orthodoxy has got the wrong end of the stick about cancer. More and more doctors agree
- Cancer, according to Professor John Beard, is a healing process that has not terminated upon completion of its task
- Clinical evidence shows a person's chances of surviving cancer are dramatically improved by making certain dietary, stress and lifestyle changes

---

[86] **Griffin, G Edward** *World Without Cancer,* www.realityzone.com

- There are at least eighteen extant cultures who do not get cancer or show almost no incidence of the disease in their society
- They have been well studied by scientists and physicians, who conclude that diets, lifestyle and lack of industrial development are responsible
- Nature has a veritable power-house of anti-cancer foods that can be used to prevent or reverse the disease
- The most potent of these are known as the nitrilosides (B17 foods)
- A 2006 Rome study showed folates are also highly effective in preventing cancer. Other studies deal with the cancer-fighting properties of magnesium and selenium
- A New York study indicated Vitamin B17 is highly effective at preventing and fighting cancer. Dr Sugiura, one of America's most eminent cancer researchers, recommended immediate further study
- His results were obfuscated and ignored
- The B Complex, including B17 (amygdalin) are excellent cancer fighters, as are Vitamins C, E and A
- Cancer patients have acidic body systems
- Societies who don't get cancer have alkali body systems
- Alkalising the body wrecks the environment cancer depends on to thrive
- Alkalising the body depends on diet, hydration and lifestyle changes
- Most cancer doctors receive almost no training in nutrition
- They rarely make reference to diet being a deciding factor in a patient's survival
- They are trained to go after the symptoms of the disease (i.e. tumours, lesions), not the underlying reason the patient got cancer in the first place

- Most orthodox cancer treatments are themselves cancer-causing/spreading
- Some chemotherapies are ex-chemical warfare agents
- Radiation causes cancer
- Cancer charities raise money for the pharmaceutical industry to come up with a drug cure or other patented treatment
- By contrast, little investment is made into researching food since there's no pay-off at the end of it
- You'd be amazed at the real cancer story
- Hopping mad too

Still, for all you CTM campaigners out there, your hard work is paying off. As we read earlier:

Good Diet Helps in Cancer Treatment

But very few sufferers are given any advice on how to improve what they eat. Barbara Lantin reports on new research that emphasises the key role of food:

'The role of a healthy diet in cancer prevention is now widely accepted - the World Cancer Research Fund's "bible" on the topic runs to 650 large pages stuffed with thousands of research citations. But until recently, little attention has been paid to the benefits of sensible eating for people who have actually received a cancer diagnosis.

However, there is growing evidence that what patients eat may affect the course of their illness. The fund's new report, due out next year, will for the first time include a chapter on nutrition and cancer survival - but this important message does not seem to be getting through to patients.'[87]

Because they're not being told. For those seeking more information on cancer, how to prevent it, and what to do if you've got it, please refer to the Credence titles:

Cancer: Why We're Still Dying to Know the Truth
Great News on Cancer in the 21st Century
B17 Metabolic Therapy - a Technical Manual
Health Wars
The ABC's of Disease

See also:
You Are What You Eat
Get in the Raw
Eat 7 g of Apricot Kernels a Day
Eat Greens
Juice Veggies
Remove Toxins From Home and Work
Exercise Prevention

---

87 *The Daily Telegraph,* 10th July 2006

- 58 -
Reduce or Eliminate Dairy

Robert Kradjian MD, Chief of the Division of General Surgery at Seton Medical Center in Daly City, California, remarks:

'Milk! Just the word itself sounds comforting. 'How about a nice cup of hot milk?' The last time you heard that question, it was from someone who cared for you, and you appreciated their effort.

The entire matter of food and especially that of milk is surrounded with emotional and cultural importance. Milk was our first food. If we were fortunate, it was our mother's milk. A loving link, given and taken. It was the only path to survival. If not mother's milk, it was cow's milk or soy milk 'formula' - rarely it was goat, camel or water buffalo milk.

Now we are a nation of milk drinkers. Nearly all of us. Infants, the young, adolescents, adults, even the elderly. We drink dozens or even several hundred gallons a year each and add to that many pounds of 'dairy' products, such as cheese, butter and yoghurt.

Can there be anything wrong with this?'[88]

Actually, plenty. The marketers of Big Milk have wooed us with their impressive campaigns of creamy moustaches and "Got Milk?" and "Milk - It Does a Body Good" in the belief milk is the greatest thing since sliced bread (which isn't a health food either). There

---

[88] **Kradjian, Robert M** *Don't Get Milk*, Seton Medical Center, #302, 1800 Sullivan Av, Daly City CA 94015 USA

is one thing conspicuously missing in the logic of their arguments, however. Bovine milk is for baby cows.

So here's the situation. Humans are the only creatures on God's Earth to get weaned off their mother's milk, only to spend the rest of their lives stuck under the udders of a completely different species. No other animal does this, let alone continues milk consumption beyond weaning and babyhood. In nature, milk will take a little animal from birth to weaning, but after that it's time for big-boy/big-girl food. No one drinks milk once they are up and running - except humans!

Harvey Diamond, author of the bestseller *Fit For Life*, sees milk as a politicised, but failing food experiment now people are wising up to the truth:

'You can be absolutely certain of one thing: Milk is the most political food in America. According to the Los Angeles Times, *the dairy industry is subsidized (meaning the taxpayer foots the bill) to the tune of almost three billion dollars a year! That's $342,000 every hour to buy hundreds of millions of dollars' worth of dairy products that will in all likelihood never be eaten.... The demand for dairy products has declined substantially, as it is becoming more apparent that they are not the perfect foods they were once touted to be.*

But dairy production is continuous. Be assured that much of the publicity referring to the health benefits of dairy products is commercially motivated. In March 1984 the Los Angeles Times *reported that the Department of Agriculture decided to launch a $140-million advertising campaign to "promote milk-drinking and help reduce the multibillion-dollar surplus." Although the real* *reason for the advertising campaign is to reduce the surplus, the ads attempt to convince you to buy milk for its many so-called health benefits.'*[89]

Milk lakes and butter mountains indicate supply of dairy completely outstrips demand. And why is that? Thousands of articles exist in the scientific and medical literature on milk (though some of the public have worked it out for themselves). Far from lauding milk as the perfect food full of calcium to make strong bones, strong teeth, 'and Olympic athletes swear by the stuff', words like 'asthma, intestinal irritation, intestinal bleeding, anaemia, diabetes, salmonella, and allergic reactions in children and infants' pepper the texts with disquieting regularity.

Toxicologists like Dr Samuel Epstein have also warned about the chronic misuse of antibiotics and hormones in cattle farming, giving rise to a whole new generation of medical issues. Increased estrogen intake brought on by farmers fattening their stock with estradiol shows links to breast and ovarian cancers, atherosclerosis and heart disease.[90] Leukaemias and lymphomas, along with arthritis, accelerated sexual development in children and the potential for infection with bovine leukaemia virus as well as childhood diabetes are also linked with excessive milk and meat consumption.[91] Contamination through the milk supply with

---

[89] Diamond, Harvey, *Fit For Life,* op. cit. pp.105-106

[90] **Epstein, Samuel S** *Politics of Cancer,* www.preventcancer.com. Estradiol, Trenbolone, Zeranol and Melengesterol Acetate are all used as hormonal anabolics in rearing cattle. Residues of these drugs are passed into the food chain with the consumption of milk and beef products. Estrogen is used because it has the ability to promote the storage of energy in the body as fat, thus increasing the weight of the animal.

[91] *American Journal of Epidemiology,* "Epidemiologic Relationships of the Bovine Population and Human Leukemia in Iowa" 112 (1980): 80 2; *Science,* "Milk of Dairy

pesticides and insecticides has also given rise to concerns, including allergy, ear and tonsillar infections, bedwetting, asthma, intestinal bleeding and colic.[92]

What a dastardly whitewash. How could the public have been so completely creamed? Harvey Diamond is right, the pro-milk pitch is not based in reality or science, it is the hype of the marketeer and the balance sheet.[93] The scientific journals are not telling us to go out and fill our swimming pools and baths with the stuff to ward off such ills milk seems perfect at preventing. In fact, Dr Frank Oski, of the Upstate Medical Center Department of Pediatrics, has spoken out against the American Academy of Pediatrics' recommendation that whole bovine milk should be consumed by infants *at all*. Breaking ranks with his peers in the scientific journal *Pediatrics,* Oski states, as the fur flies around his ears:

'It is my thesis that milk should not be fed to the infant in the first year of life because of its association with iron deficiency anaemia (cow's milk is so deficient in iron that an infant would have to consume an impossible 31 quarts a day to get the iron RDA of 15mg), occult gastrointestinal bleeding, and various manifestations of food allergy. I further suggest that unmodified whole bovine milk should not be consumed after infancy because of the problems of lactose intolerance, its contribution to the genesis of atherosclerosis, and its possible link to other diseases.'[94]

Cows Frequently Contains a Leukemogenic Virus" 213 (1981): 1014 3

[92] *Pediatrics,* "Is Bovine Milk a Health Hazard?" Suppl. 75:182-186; 1985

[93] *Lancet 2,* "Beware of the Cow" (editorial), (1974): 30 4

[94] *Pediatrics,* 1983: 72-253

Most milk moustachers don't realise milk contains blood and white (pus) cells from the animal. USDA inspectors in America simply ask processing companies to keep the content of these to a maximum of 1 to 1.5 million white cells per millilitre (1/30th of an ounce) to avoid immune system problems. The other pertinent point, before we suckle another of our favourite dairy dishes, is that fifty years ago, the average cow produced 20,000 pounds of milk per annum. Today, the top gold-star bovines are churning out 50,000-plus pounds by comparison. Do you want to know how the cows are able to do this? Charles Atlas' Dynamic Tension Technique maybe? An LA Sports Club membership perhaps?

Antibiotics, drugs and recombinant Bovine Growth Hormone (rBGH), a genetically engineered drug produced by Monsanto (which swears blind it doesn't affect the milk or meat of the animal). Beef hormones are big business because they fatten cows, which means farmers want to buy the hormones, since, in the case of estradiol, they add significant weight to an animal during its 100-day fattening period prior to slaughter, resulting in an extra $80-odd in the farmer's wallet. Dr Epstein describes a frightening legacy of non-regulation and governmental irresponsibility in the US:

'As of 1990, more than 95% of American beef cattle were implanted with carcinogenic, growth-promoting hormones. The European Economic Community banned hormone-treated meat in 1989, and does not allow US or other producers to export their meat into the EEC. This ban was upheld by a World Trade Organisation appellate body (February 1998).

In the absence of effective federal regulation, the US meat industry uses hundreds of animal feed additives, including antibiotics, tranquilizers, pesticides, animal drugs, artificial flavours, industrial wastes, and growth-promoting hormones, with little or no concern about the carcinogenic and other toxic effects of dietary residues of these additives.'[95]

So what's the big deal? Cow's milk is similar to human milk, isn't it? Not by a long slurp. The calcium the cow gets from the grass is packed into coarse calcium to build baby cows into big ones. Humans find coarse calcium hard to break down (calcium stones, etc). America, the world's top dairy consumer, has one of the highest levels of osteoporosis in the world, so someone's telling white lies and not coming clean with the public.

Milk components vary widely according to species. Cow's milk, for instance, has three to four times more protein than human milk. Rat milk contains up to eleven times more protein than human milk.[96] Cow's milk is designed to assist baby cows in their development in very specific ways. It has five to seven times the mineral content but is markedly deficient in essential fatty acids and iron when compared to human mothers' milk, which contains up to eleven times the essential fatty acid components, most specifically linoleic acid, essential for neurological development, completely removed from cow's milk when skimmed.[97] (Cows are not famous for their mental gymnastics).

Harvey Diamond points out other problems: *'The enzymes required to break down and digest milk are renin and lactase. They*

---

95 Epstein, Samuel S, *Politics...* op. cit. p.585

96 **Bell, G** *Textbook of Physiology and Biochemistry*, Baltimore: Williams & Wilkins, 1959

97 **Kradjian, Robert M** *Don't Get Milk*, Seton Medical Center, #302, 1800 Sullivan Av, Daly City CA 94015 USA

are all but gone by the age of three in most humans. There is a protein in all milk known as casein. There is three hundred times more casein in cow's milk than in human's milk. That's for the development of huge bones. Casein coagulates in the stomach and forms large, tough, dense, difficult-to-digest curds that are adapted to the four-stomach digestive apparatus of a cow.

Once inside the human system, this thick mass of goo puts a tremendous burden on the body to get rid of it somehow. In other words, a huge amount of energy must be expended in dealing with it. Unfortunately some of this gooey substance hardens and adheres to the lining of the intestines and prevents the absorption of nutrients into the body. Also the by-products of milk digestion leave a great deal of toxic mucus in the body. It's very acidic, and it is stored in the body until it can be dealt with at a later time. The next time you are going to dust your home, smear some paste all over everything and see how easy it is to dust. Dairy products do the same inside your body. That translates into more weight instead of weight loss. Casein, by the way, is the base of one of the strongest glues used in woodworking.'[98]

What am I saying here, *that a splash of milk in tea or coffee is a sin now?* I'm saying if milk-drinking had anything to do with logic, we should be drinking *human mother's milk.* We should have factories up and down the country full up with women connected up to industrial milking machines.

Actually, I'm trying to stop you drinking gallons of the stuff in the belief it's giving you some sort of health benefit. Now, if you

---

[98] Diamond, Harvey, op. cit. pp.107-108

bristle and say, *'Well, I like it!'* then you've probably got the best reason for continuing as you are if you don't feel the need to change. For others suffering from chronic sinus or digestion problems, a detailed working of this luscious subject can be found in the **Health Wars** chapter, *White Lies and Porky Pies.* Also you can check out the eponymous **www.notmilk.com** if you're prepared to lose your bottle.

- 57 -
Exercise Your Eyesight

Yes, do.

Most short sight is not 'an affliction', it's how your eyesight has adjusted to what you use it the most for. Also, far-sightedness, poor night vision, 'Middle-age' sight (reading glasses), crossed eye (strabismus), lazy eye (amblyopia), and sensitivity to light, eyestrain, headaches and burning eyes can all be improved if you decide to invest some effort.

The spectacles industry adopts the usual strategy of sticking expensive glasses on your nose without rectifying the underlying cause of the problem - we're getting used to the pattern now. Avoid LASIK surgery (Laser-Assisted In Situ Keratomileusis), touted as the quick fix. See www.surgicaleyes.org for the ones that went wrong. www.mercola.com has a great natural program you can use while you go about your daily business (type in 'eyesight').

As a writer, I'm sometimes as blind as a bat after a protracted project, having stared at a computer screen for hours on end. Short of taking up quill and inkpot (which doesn't correct the short-range problem), it's my occupational hazard, so I compensate with shorter writing hours and indulging in hobbies which require a completely different use for my eyes. After a few weeks, my vision adjusts and I can say, after writing twelve books with five more in the pipeline, that my vision is above average. Always room for improvement, though.

Diet affects eyesight greatly. An over-consumption of hydrogenated vegetable oils and transfats can lead to a condition known as macular degeneration. Mercola recommends four steps as you age:

- Take fish oils (Omega 3's)
- Get plenty of lutein, a carotenoid found in vegetables and fruits
- Eat dark-coloured berries, rich in bioflavonoids (a Vitamin C component), which strengthen capillaries
- Avoid unhealthy fats

My tips are:

- Have a good diet
- Get at least two hours outside each day focusing on long-distance objects, then others close up
- Get plenty of sleep
- Avoid stress
- Don't strain to focus, do the opposite - *relax*

See also:
You Are What You Eat
Be an Overcomer
Supplement Real Vitamin C
Turn Off the TV
There's Danger in Excess, Moderation in All Things
Get Enough Sleep
Avoid Medical Testing Disease
Avoid Repetitive Strain

~ 56 ~
Sprout!

Grow seeds at home, effortlessly, dirt-cheap, for a healthy, nutritious boost to your daily intake.

Steve Meyerowitz is the green-caped Sproutman, cajoling the world into adopting healthier, self-reliant eating practices. You can tell his enthusiasm is home-grown and organic:

'Not all of us can be gardeners, but we all eat. Fact is, if you don't grow your own, someone has to do it for you. Not a bad concept, but in reality, we're on the losing end. A trip to the supermarket proves it. The lettuce is lifeless; the spinach is wilting and dark around the edges. You don't dare eat the fruit for fear of fumigants, fertilizers, pesticides and the like. As a nation, we're eating less and less of the healthiest foods on the planet.

Where are the fruits and vegetables? For the most part, in the canned food aisle. No wonder kids grow up never liking their vegetables! Of course, you could shop at the health food store, but organic produce sometimes costs more than you want to spend - if you can find it at all. Unfortunately, we don't all live in southern California and we don't all have the time or means to garden.

Here's where apartment gardening comes in. Every week a new harvest of fresh baby greens matures right in your own kitchen. No tools to buy, no big investment in garden equipment, no bugs or weather to worry about and no dirt. One pound of indoor lettuce takes up just 9 inches of counter-top space and one actual minute of care per day. Just dip and set. Light is no problem - normal daylight is all you need. For such little effort, the possibilities are magnificent - 30 delicious varieties of fresh, nutritious indoor greens and baby vegetables, enough to feed the whole family!'[99]

Alfalfa, mung, broccoli, radish - all those little darlings waiting for lift-off - not forgetting the king-daddy of weeds, wheatgrass.

'The path to health starts with a major cleaning,' the Sprouted One continues. *'If there is infestation, you have to control it. If there is damage, you have to reconstruct. First stop the poisoning of the blood and tissues from acidifying diet, bacteria, yeast, giardia and parasites. Reverse the trend of acidification and alkalize with wheatgrass juice and an enzyme-rich living-foods diet. Take nothing from a box or can. Eat from the garden. Eliminate sugar except when it comes inside a fruit. Throw out the espresso machine and the microwave and put a juicer and blender in their place.*

Clear the blockages, empty the garbage and reinvigorate the elimination system with colon hydrotherapy. Jump-start the liver with a massage and wheatgrass implant. You can change. Your body is a milky-way of trillions of cells which combine to make up tissues and glands. But every minute we breathe in new atoms and exhale the old. In six weeks, every atom in your liver is replaced. Renewal is a constant. What foods will you renew with? Stop treating your stomach like a compost heap and start treating it like a garden. Set in motion an upward cycle of rejuvenation that leads to balanced health. The signposts are: trimmer weight,

---

99 **Meyerowitz, Steve** *Sprouts - The Miracle Food,* Sproutman Publications, 1999. Available from the Credence Store at www.credence.org

clearer mind, brighter eyes, better concentration, more energy and vitality!'

There you have it, straight from a superhero.

Credence does a great idiot-proof, electric auto-sprouter, which gives perfect results every time. I fill up the tank with fresh water, sprinkle the seeds onto the trays, plug in and switch on. I change the water daily and harvest the crop five days later. Sam and I have eradicated a portion of our food bill simply by making changes to the choices we make.

Get growing!

A good educational project for the kids too!

- 55 -
Don't Gamble

Gambling: a tax on people who are bad at maths

One lottery ticket - not what I'm talking about.

A fistful of lottery tickets, scratch-cards, Lucky 8's, and two hours a night on the pokey machines is what I'm talking about.

Serious gambling is an addiction, so telling you to stop is not going to cut the mustard. See **Deal With Addictions** to find out how these patterns are installed and what you can do about them. Politically, the gambling industry wields some big clout, including John Prescott. We also appreciate this phenomenon in the incongruity of Tony Blair confessing his care for us at the same time he's signing off on the introduction of super-casinos into Britain.

Now don't go thinking there's anything wrong with the occasional flutter at Ascot. What's good enough for Her Majesty the Queen is good enough for *paysans* like us. Then again, has the flutter become a steady drone in your household? Is gambling a problem you won't admit to? It's one of the fastest-growing money-makers on the Internet and many are already hooked with the ease with which bets can be placed - and lost. If you have a problem, deal with it before it ruins you, your spouse, your family, and everything you've spent a lifetime to accumulate.

Goodness, if I were prime minister.

- You wouldn't want me as prime minister.

See also:

You're Never Too Old to Change
Limit Caffeine, Alcohol and Carbonated Drinks
Supplement Real Vitamin C
Admit When You're Wrong
Deal With Chronic Issues
Work at Self-Improvement
There's Danger in Excess, Moderation in All Things
Give Yourself Permission to Recover
Deal With Addictions
Take Responsibility For Your Actions
Help Others

- 54 -
Take a Basic Supplement Program

Due to over-farming, much of the commercial land our food is grown in is depleted of minerals. Mineral-poor foods coupled with stressful lifestyles produce the worst kind of results - heart attacks, strokes, cancer and diabetes.

Warwick Town Council, UK, laments: *'Over the last 50 years, vegetables sold in the UK have lost 24% of their magnesium, 27% of their iron and 46% of their calcium. Isn't it time to stop the rot? Jamie Oliver's 'School Dinners', Rick Stein's 'Food Heroes', Hugh Fearnley Whittingstall's field-to-table fare at River Cottage - the message is all around us that good food, nutrition and health go hand-in-hand, and we must eat more fresh, unprocessed foods. But no one admits that the cause of our poor health and social disorders is not just fast foods, but the source of our foods.'*

Warwick's righteous because Graham Harvey's in town with his book. Harvey is best known for shaking up the farming community by shining a harsh light on how they produce our food. *We Want Real Food* is an absolute must-read (available through Amazon). In *Health Wars* and the *ABC's of Disease*, I cover in detail the problems of vitamin and mineral depletion in our diets, as well as enzyme and antioxidant deficiency, and while we're at it, selenium, omega 3 and magnesium.

Industrial farming uses tons of nitrate fertilizer which wrecks the soil for the sake of more tons and bushels per acre. And that's before you get me started on that Everest of idiocy, genetically modified 'terminator' crops. The mineral depletion of soils was a pressing issue back in the 1930's in the US, so much so that a Senate document was drafted to sound the klaxon. It's worth quoting the main passage in light of the fact that nothing was subsequently done.

'Our physical well-being is more directly dependent upon minerals we take into our systems than upon calories or vitamins, or upon precise proportions of starch, protein or carbohydrates we consume... Do you know that most of us today are suffering from certain dangerous diet deficiencies which cannot be remedied until depleted soils from which our food comes are brought into proper mineral balance?

The alarming fact is that foods (fruits, vegetables and grains), now being raised on millions of acres of land that no longer contain enough of certain minerals, are starving us - no matter how much of them we eat. No man of today can eat enough fruits and vegetables to supply his system with the minerals he requires for perfect health because his stomach isn't big enough to hold them.

You'd think, wouldn't you, that a carrot is a carrot - that one is about as good as another as far as nourishment is concerned? But it isn't; one carrot may look and taste like another and yet be lacking in the particular mineral element which our system requires and which carrots are supposed to contain.

Laboratory test prove that the fruits, the vegetables, the grains, the eggs, and even the milk and the meats of today are not what they were a few generations ago (which doubtless explains why our forefathers thrived on a selection of foods that would starve us!)

No man today can eat enough fruits and vegetables to supply his stomach with the mineral salts he requires for perfect health, because his stomach isn't big enough to hold them!

No longer does a balanced and fully nourishing diet consist merely of so many calories or certain vitamins or fixed proportion of starches, proteins and carbohydrates. We know that our diets must contain in addition something like a score of minerals salts.

It is bad news to learn from our leading authorities that 99% of the American people are deficient in these minerals [this was in 1936!], *and that a marked deficiency in any one of the more important minerals actually results in disease. Any upset of the balance, any considerable lack or one or another element, however microscopic the body requirement may be, and we sicken, suffer, shorten our lives.*

We know that vitamins are complex chemical substances which are indispensable to nutrition, and that each of them is of importance for normal function of some special structure in the body. Disorder and disease result from any vitamin deficiency. It is not commonly realized, however, that vitamins control the body's appropriation of minerals, and in the absence of minerals they have no function to perform. Lacking vitamins, the system can make some use of minerals, but lacking minerals, vitamins are useless. Certainly our physical well-being is more directly dependent upon the minerals we take into our systems than upon calories of vitamins or upon the precise proportions of starch, protein of carbohydrates we consume.

This discovery is one of the latest and most important contributions of science to the problem of human health.'[100]

More recently, David Thomas's detailed research on British soils since WW2 is an eye-opener.[101] The results go a long way to explaining the problems and why a balanced whole-food diet, the majority eaten raw, together with a supplement program, can have such a dramatic effect. The supplementation I have used for years has kept me disease-free for over two decades and consists of the following four items:

- Minerals (Neways Maximol)
- Antioxidants (Neways Revenol)
- Vitamin C complex (powdered with bioflavonoids, Credence store)
- Essential Fatty Acids (must include filtered fish oils)
- Apricot kernels (Credence store or your local supplier) - make sure they're bitter

See a **Guide to Nutritional Supplements** in *The ABC's of Disease* for more information on the essentials.

See also:
You Are What You Eat
Get in the Raw
Eat Apricot Kernels Each Day
Supplement with Vitamin C
Drink Two Litres of Water a Day
There's Danger in Excess, Moderation in All Things

---

[100] Senate Document No. 264, 1936, 74th Congress, 2nd Session
[101] http://www.positivehealth.com/PERMIT/ARTICLES/Nutrition/marsh69.htm

- 53 -

Don't Lose Your Joy

'False, lying, cowardly, nauseous puppy. The greatest ass, liar and beast in the world.'

- King George III, on his eldest son, Prince Frederick

'I wish the ground would open up this minute and sink the monster into the lowest hole in hell.'

- Queen Caroline, on her eldest son, Prince Frederick

Don't get back home on a Friday night, open the mail, cringe at the phone bill and have it wreck your entire weekend. Instead, call up the phone company and ask 'Why, in a country of free speech, is there a bloody phone bill at all?' Don't lurch from one crisis to another. If this is you, you're suffering from patterning which needs to be overwritten.

Many worry. I don't. We're all going to die one day but at least I won't already have died the death of a thousand cuts over things a) I've no control over, and b) I've long since forgotten about.

How about you?

- Be joyful
- Enjoy those overwhelming, optimistic experiences
- Train yourself to toughen up to weather grim times
- These things too shall pass
- There's little you're going through that nobody else is
- For heaven's sake take a holiday

NEXT!

- 52 -

Avoid Pork

And shellfish, hydrogenated fats and unfermented soy

There are foods that really shouldn't be foods. Pork is a major mischief-maker and homotoxin. In a study entitled 'The Adverse Influence of Pork Consumption on Health', Professor Hans-Heinrich Reckeweg states:

'The fact that pork causes stress and gives rise to poisoning is known. It is obvious that this does not only apply to preparations of fresh pork such as cold cuts, knuckles, feet, ribs and cutlets, etc., but also to cured meats (ham, bacon, etc.) and to smoked meats prepared for sausages.

Consumption of freshly killed pork products causes acute responses, such as inflammations of the appendix and gall bladder, biliary colics, acute intestinal catarrh, gastroenteritis with typhoid and paratyphoid symptoms, as well as acute eczema, carbuncles, sudoriparous abscesses, and others. These symptoms can be observed after consuming sausage meats (including salami which contains pieces of bacon in the form of fat).

The consumption of pork is particularly dangerous in the tropical regions. This, for example, is shown in parts of Africa where both the Islamic and Western civilizations live in neighboring territories under the same climatic conditions. The same conditions apply to various races in the Himalayas where the Hunsa (Bircher) live. The Islamic population does not consume pork and is healthy, working to a considerable age as porters for numerous expeditions.

The races of the Western civilizations living on the other side of the valley do not observe the Islamic rules of behaviour and eating, and suffer from all of the common illnesses. In other words, the population which observes the Islamic laws is healthy, while those who follow the habits of western civilization manifest all the typical diseases which come with the consumption of pork. Reference must be made to the founders of the great cultures, who have also fundamentally influenced Western culture. Moses, the prophet, and Mohammed, for example, recognized the prohibitions imposed by nature and based their laws on them.'[102]

A master butcher will tell you, when they cut pork carcasses they often find maggots, worms and tumours. As Reckeweg states, the Jews also proscribed the consumption of pork as part of Levitican law, not for symbolic reasons, but on sanitary grounds to keep disease out of the camps. Dr Ted Broer warns pork products are packed with nitrites, which can cause high blood urea and dikitopiprazines, leading to brain tumours and leukaemia.[103]

Avoid Shellfish

...the scavengers of the sea, which collect toxins (mercury from pollutants especially) and pass them on consumers. The same goes for filter-feeders like oysters, whelks, mussels, etc. Studies show shellfish can contain parasites and drug-resistant bacteria, and farmed beasties are far worse:[104]

---

[102] *Biologic Therapy,* Vol 1, No 2, 1983;
text at http://www.moseshand.com/studies/eatingpork.htm

[103] Day, Phillip, *Food for Thought,* op. cit.

[104] Annual Meeting of the American Society for Microbiology in Salt Lake City, May 2002. www.mercola.com

'[Consumption of] *some exotic animals... can lead to severe nerve problems and gastrointestinal disorders, a new British study has recently cautioned. "People should exercise caution whenever confronted with a plate of exotic shellfish or large tropical fish," one of the researchers said. Toxins in moray eels, puffer fish, and a variety of shellfish have been linked to a number of health problems among travellers and coastal inhabitants throughout Asia.*[105]

So lay off the puffer fish.

* * * * *

Avoid Partially and Fully Hydrogenated Fats

Researchers Mary Enig and Sally Fallon write: '[Hydrogenation] *is the process that turns polyunsaturates, normally liquid at room temperature, into fats that are solid at room temperature - i.e. margarine and shortening. To produce them, manufacturers begin with the cheapest oils - soy, corn, cottonseed or canola, already rancid from the extraction process - and mix them with tiny metal particles - usually nickel oxide.*

The oil with its nickel catalyst is then subjected to hydrogen gas in a high-pressure, high-temperature reactor. Next, soap-like emulsifiers and starch are squeezed into the mixture to give it a better consistency; the oil is yet again subjected to high temperatures when it is steam-cleaned.

This removes its unpleasant odour. Margarine's natural colour, an unappetizing grey, is removed by bleach. Dyes and strong

---

[105] http://www.sciencedaily.com/releases/2005/03/050326002349.htm

flavours must then be added to make it resemble butter. Finally, the mixture is compressed and packaged in blocks or tubs and sold as a health food.

Partially hydrogenated margarines and shortenings are even worse for you than the highly refined vegetable oils from which they are made because of chemical changes that occur during the hydrogenation process. Under high temperatures, the nickel catalyst causes the hydrogen atoms to change position on the fatty acid chain....

The cause of heart disease is not animal fats and cholesterol but rather a number of factors inherent in modern diets, including excess consumption of vegetables oils and hydrogenated fats; excess consumption of refined carbohydrates in the form of sugar and white flour; mineral deficiencies, particularly low levels of protective magnesium and iodine; deficiencies of vitamins, particularly of vitamin C, needed for the integrity of the blood vessel walls, and of antioxidants like selenium and vitamin E, which protect us from free radicals. And, finally, the disappearance of antimicrobial fats from the food supply - namely, animal fats and tropical oils.'[106]

They are, of course, talking of the problems with fake butters, margarine, and a whole host of modern 'conveniences', which are not really food at all. Better butter in meager amounts, though if you are lactose intolerant or exhibiting stomach and digestion problems, you'd do well to steer clear of dairy completely.

* * * * *

---

[106] http://www.mercola.com/2002/aug/21/saturated_fat2.htm

Avoid Unfermented Soy

I'm not going to enhance my popularity here by having a go at soy, but a spade's a spade and there are some definite problems.

Sean McNary Carson writes: *'As the soy industry lobbied the Food and Drug Administration for a cardiovascular health claim for soy protein, two senior FDA scientists, Daniel Sheehan and Daniel Doerge - both specialists in estrogen research - wrote a letter vigorously opposing such a claim. In fact, they suggested a warning might be more appropriate. Their concern? Two isoflavones found in soy, genistein and daidzen, the same two promoted by the industry for everything from menopause relief to cancer protection, were said to "demonstrate toxicity in estrogen sensitive tissues and in the thyroid."*

Moreover, "adverse effects in humans occur in several tissues and, apparently, by several distinct mechanisms." Sheehan also quoted a landmark study (Cassidy, et al. 1994), showing that as little as 45 mg of isoflavones could alter the length of a pre-menopausal woman's menstrual cycle. The scientists were particularly concerned about the effects of these two plant estrogens on foetuses and young infants, because "development is recognised as the most sensitive life stage for estrogen toxicity.[107]

Today, hypothyroidism (underactive thyroid) is widespread. How much of this is down to soy consumption, no-one's yet put a figure on it. While the Amazon's being hacked away to produce hundreds of square miles of soy, the public continues believing the bean is the food of the ancients, even citing the longevity of

---

[107] Day, Phillip, *Food For Thought*, op. cit.

Asian cultures to justify it as a health food. The reality is, what we term 'soy' is not even the same stuff they're eating. Sean Carson again:

'Oddly, nowhere in industry promotion does anyone differentiate between traditional, painstakingly prepared "Asian" soy foods and the modern, processed items that Fallon calls "imitation food." And therein lies the rub. Modern soy protein foods in no way resemble the traditional Asian soy foods, and may contain carcinogens like nitrates, lysinoalanine, as well as a number of anti-nutrients which are only significantly degraded by fermentation or other traditional processing.

So, while Asians were using limited to moderate amounts of painstakingly prepared soy foods - the alleged benefits of which are still controversial - Americans, especially vegetarians, are consuming more soy products and isoflavones than any culture in human history, and as one researcher put it, "entering a great unknown." [108]

New Zealand-based Soyonlineservice.co.nz introduces us to the dark side of the bean: *'Have you ever wondered about soy? It's promoted as the miracle food that will feed the world while at the same time preventing and curing all manner of diseases. But what if all you've read about soy is nothing but a multi-million dollar marketing strategy based on scanty facts, half-truths and lies? How could anyone get away with that?*

The soy industry is one of the world's most wealthy and powerful and one that will steamroller anyone who dares suggest

---

[108] www.campaignfortruth.com

there may be problems. When we first questioned the safety of soy, a representative of Protein Technologies told us they had: "...teams of lawyers to crush dissenters, could buy scientists to give evidence, owned television channels and newspapers, could divert medical schools and even influence governments..." A boast which has proven all too true. You'll be shocked to learn that much of what you've read about soy is nothing but a con.'

The Whole Soy Story: The Dark Side of America's Favorite Health Food is a book out by Dr Kaayla Daniel, available through Dr Joseph Mercola's web-site (www.mercola.com). A must for anyone consuming soy products on a daily basis. In it, you'll learn soy is not the health panacea it's touted to be, nor the answer to world hunger, nor even disease-prevention. In fact, soy has not even been proved safe. Dr Daniel explains how –

- Soy impedes the sexual maturation of boys (p. 335)
- Soy accelerates the sexual maturation of girls (p. 339)
- In newborns, the hormonal effects of soy may be irreversible (p. 333)
- The average daily dose of soy estrogens in soy formula (38mg) is higher than the amounts that cause thyroid problems and endocrine disruption *in adults* (p. 334)

Please check out this book and the following sites if you need to know more:

www.soyonlineservice.co.nz

http://thedoctorwithin.com/index_fr.php?page=articles/magic_bean.php

www.mercola.com

www.campaignfortruth.com

~ 51 ~
Be In Love

*'The quickest way to a man's heart
is through his chest.'* - **Roseanne Barr**

Love hurts, but our lives are completely the poorer without it. Romance novels are bestsellers. *Hello* and *OK* magazines outstrip their competitors preoccupying their readership with what went wrong, who loaded the gun, who got the cat, etc., Yet love remains one of life's most sacred experiences in spite of the cynics, transcending expression, inviting eulogies from the likes of Shelley, Shakespeare and Phyllis Diller.

The fact that sometimes love doesn't go right makes it all the more precious when it does. Humans, by their very need for love, are not meant to live alone. We love, procreate, take pride in raising our children. Don't give up on this amazing, primal force.

- Love is the expression of the eternal mind
- Love says, 'It doesn't get better than this'
- Love is never admitting yours is the most dysfunctional family on Earth
- William Mizner can't get over the embarrassing fact he was born in bed with a woman
- The highlight of Garrison Keillor's childhood was making his brother laugh so hard the food came out of his nose

We're born, we love, we die.

God is love.

~ 50 ~
Join CTM For Regular Updates

The Campaign for Truth in Medicine

Want to know more about these and other fascinating subjects? Let me invite you to catapult the *Simple Changes* message far and wide across the world by joining the Campaign for Truth in Medicine. Public pressure - united and determined - always wins out, and by joining the ranks of thousands already making a difference, you'll be doing your bit to usher in a happier, healthier 21st Century.

Joining the Campaign is free and can be done via our web-site at www.campaignfortruth.com. Once a month, you will receive EClub via the Internet where these and other subjects are discussed as the news breaks and vested interests slip on the flak jackets.

See also:
Be An Overcomer
Strive for Excellence
Attack Political Correctness
Work at Self-Improvement
Exercise Prevention
Obtain Control Over Your Sense of Certainty
Be Inspired
Experience Success
Start Complaining
Take Responsibility For Your Actions
Help Others

- 49 -
Get Enough Sleep

In the age of Internet and drinking and gambling around the clock, the advice to get your head down by 10:30 pm might seem a tad quaint and motherly. But the body needs sleep and if you don't oblige it - well, sleep debt is also one of the chief causes of road accidents in the US (as well as driving on the wrong side of the road).

Being exposed to artificial light and/or staying up for long periods at night both increase the risk of breast cancer, according to a study by the American National Cancer Institute and the National Institute of Environmental Health Sciences.[109] It is thought unsociable hours disrupt the production of the neurotransmitter hormone melatonin, which is excreted by the pineal gland mostly at night and regulates everything from your hormones and digestive cycles to sleeping and waking rhythms. Simply put, if you aren't sleeping in pitch darkness, the brain is fooled into thinking dawn is around the corner when she's not. She went home for an early night just as you should have done, boyo.

Details, Details

If you're interested in this subject, a good book to get is TS Wiley and Bent Formby's *Lights Out - Sleep, Sugar and Survival.* An Amazon book review declares: *'After probing the scientific literature, Wiley and Formby, researchers at the Sansum Medical Research Institute, conclude that "the disastrous slide in the health of the American people corresponds to the increase in*

[109] Cancer Causes & Control, May 2006;17(4):515-23

light-generating night activities and the carbohydrate consumption that follows." Our internal clocks are governed by seasonal variations in light and dark; extending daylight artificially leads to a craving for sugar, especially concentrated, refined carbohydrates that, in turn, cause obesity. More seriously, lack of sleep inhibits the production of prolactin and melatonin - deranging the immune system and causing depression, diabetes, heart disease, and cancer. The authors prescribe sleeping at least nine and a half hours in total darkness in the fall and winter and switching to a diet low in carbohydrates and high in protein, vegetables, and healthy fats. They support their arguments with 100 pages of notes and by tracing the progression of disease from hunter-gatherers to our high-tech society. Despite its somewhat strident, all-knowing tone, this illuminating work is highly recommended for academic and public libraries.'[110]

Some Tips

- Get heavier curtains to block out any light
- Be consistent with your sleep periods
- If you have to get up during the night, try doing so without turning on the light
- Don't fall over the dog or down the stairs

Night Loops

The Health Ranger reports:

- *'Children who have symptoms of Attention Deficit/Hyperactive Disorder (ADHD) actually may be sleep-deprived, according to researchers at the Technion-Israel Institute of Technology Sleep Laboratory*

---

[110] Ilse Heidmann, www.amazon.com, search under book title

- *An estimated 8 percent of US children suffer from ADHD, according to the US Centers for Disease Control, and more than half of them are being treated with drugs*
- *ADHD is characterized by over-alertness and nervousness, with affected children being fidgety and over-stimulated*
- *Half of the test subjects with ADHD (vs. 22 percent of the control group) suffered from some degree of sleep-disordered breathing, such as sleep apnea, which is characterized by interruptions in breathing that last 10 seconds or more, occurring at least five times per hour during sleep*
- *Fifteen percent (vs. none in the control group) had Periodic Limb Movement Disorder (PLMD), which is relatively uncommon among children*
- *For example, school performance, which is low in children with sleep apnea, has been found to improve markedly following the removal of adenoids and tonsils to correct the disorder*
- *The researchers urge parents of hyperactive and attention-deficit children diagnosed with sleep disorders to have breathing irregularities and limb movements treated, to enforce good sleeping habits, and to avoid giving them caffeinated drinks at night'*[111]

Dr Mercola advises:

- *'Breast cancer risk was higher among women who often did not sleep during the period of the night when levels of the sleep-regulating hormone melatonin are typically at their highest, the study indicates. Their breast cancer risk increased 14% for each night of the week that they reported not sleeping during this period*

---

[111] www.newstarget.com, search under sleep.
Study at http://health.dailynewscentral.com/content/view/1664/

- *Working the graveyard shift upped a woman's risk of developing breast cancer by 60%*
- *The results of this study provide evidence that indicators of exposure to light at night may be associated with the risk of developing breast cancer*
- *Researchers from Harvard Medical School also examined the relationship between breast cancer and working the night shift in more than 78,000 nurses*
- *Women who worked between 1 and 29 years on a rotating night-shift schedule had an 8% increase in breast cancer risk, while women who worked 30 or more years on the night shift showed a 36% increase in their risk of developing breast cancer*[112]

---

[112] www.mercola.com

~ 48 ~
Reduce or Eliminate Red Meat

'Pembrook, the renegade third Wright brother, immediately set to work on the first anti-aircraft gun.' – **Sydney Harris**

The first thing to appreciate is how much more meat protein we as a society are eating when compared with the average westernised diet before World War 2. In fact, chronic meat-eating by Western populations is only a relatively recent fad. Back in the medieval times, meat was a luxury few could afford. The average peasant subsisted on a largely vegetarian diet. He didn't kill his cows because he wanted the milk. He didn't kill his chickens because he wanted the eggs. Straying into the King's parks to poach some venison or rabbit would, likely as not if you were caught, see you twisting in the wind by sunset.

Excessive meat-eating, according to researcher Ethel R Nelson MD, is at the root of many of today's health woes:

'For the past twenty-five years, researchers in human nutrition have pointed to the unrefined plant dietary as a more ideal food than animal products. They have designated the Western world's high-fat animal product, fibre-poor, refined diet as the chief cause of so-called "Western diseases", e.g. coronary heart disease, diabetes, obesity, gallstones, appendicitis, diverticulosis of the bowel, hiatus hernia, hemorrhoids, osteoporosis, kidney disorders, varicose veins, cancer, and accelerated sexual development in children.

Some of today's most prevalent and devastating diseases in the United States have now been credited to excessive consumption of meat and animal products (milk, cheese, eggs) and insufficient ingestion of plant foods.'[113]

As Harvey Diamond explains, humans are not natural carnivores:

'A carnivore's teeth are long sharp and pointed - all of them! We have molars for crushing and grinding. A carnivore's jaws move up and down only, for tearing and biting. Ours can move from side to side for grinding. A carnivore's saliva is acid and geared to the digestion of animal protein; it lacks ptyalin, a chemical that digests starches. Our saliva is alkaline and contains ptyalin for the digestion of starch. A carnivore's stomach is a simple, round sack that secretes ten times more hydrochloric acid than that of a non-carnivore. Our stomachs are oblong in shape, complicated in structure, and convoluted with a duodenum.

A carnivore's intestines are three times the length of its trunk, designed for rapid expulsion of animal proteins, which quickly rot. Our intestines are twelve times the length of our trunks and designed to keep food in them until all nutrients are extracted. The liver of a carnivore is capable of eliminating ten to fifteen times more uric acid than the liver of a non-carnivore. Our livers have the capacity to eliminate only a small amount of uric acid. Uric acid is an extremely dangerous toxic substance that can wreak havoc in your body. All meat consumption releases large quantities of uric acid into the system. Unlike most carnivores and omnivores, humans do not have the enzyme uricase to break down uric acid.

---

113 **Nelson, Ethel R** *The Eden Diet and Modern Nutritional Research*, the Twin Cities Creation Conference, Northwestern College, 1992

A carnivore does not sweat through the skin and has no pores. We do sweat through the skin and have pores. A carnivore's urine is acid. Ours is alkaline. A carnivore's tongue is rough, ours is smooth. Our hands are perfectly designed for plucking fruit from a tree, not for tearing the guts out of the carcass of a dead animal as are a carnivore's claws.'[114]

I'm Gagging For It

If the above doesn't convince you humans are not natural carnivores, then trust to instinct. What are you *psychologically* programmed to eat? Next time you drive over some road kill, screech to a halt, leap out with your juices flowing and go back and get stuck into the blood and guts. Tear that rabbit apart and delight and marvel as the blood flows down your throat. Feel the satisfying crunch of its bones and the slippery visceral sensation of its organs in your mouth. Well, why not? You're a meat-eater by instinct, aren't you? Any of your brothers and sisters-in-kin, like a fox or a crow or even a dog, would likely beat you to it. Don't be the runt of the pack! Get your muzzle in there, snap aside the competition, and chow on down!

And, while you're at it, leap over the fence when you're done and go and suckle a few of those Jerseys over there to slake that rabid thirst. Don't worry about the cars that have pulled over, their occupants staring in ghastly fascination. They're just a jealous bunch of failed meat- and milk-swillers wishing they had come along and got tuckered down a minute or two before you did.

---

[114] **Diamond, Harvey** *Fit For Life,* Bantam Books, 1984, pp.97-98

Don't Pass This Way Again

Nutritionist Dr Dean Burkitt also accuses the West's fibre-deficient, refined diet of causing modern Western diseases.[115] Burkitt and colleague Alec Walker determined, by studying multiple bowel transit times, that meat-heavy, ill-combined meals were creating an aftermath of appendicitis, constipation, diverticulosis, varicose veins, haemorrhoids and colon cancer (the second leading cancer death). They found the average time for passage for this putrefying detritus through the gut was three to five days, and even as much as two weeks in the elderly. Rural Third World peoples, on the other hand, consuming diets fibre-rich in unrefined plant dietary, such as yams, cassava, cereals, vegetables and fruits, with little animal products, passed easily propelled stools in 24 to 36 hours.[116]

William J Mayo, founder of the famous Mayo cancer clinic in the United States, addressed the American College of Surgeons thus: *'Meat-eating has increased 400% in the last 100 years. Cancer of the stomach forms nearly one third of all cancers of the human body. If flesh foods are not fully broken up, decomposition results, and active poisons are thrown into an organ not intended for their reception.'*[117]

---

115 **Burkitt, D P** *Don't Forget Fibre in Your Diet*, London: Martin Dunitz Ltd., 1979

116 **Walker, A R P, Burkitt & Painter** *Lancet 2*, "Effect of Dietary Fibre on Stools and Transit-Times, and Its Role in the Causation of Disease", (1972): pp.1408-1412

117 **Leonardo, Blanche** *Cancer and Other Diseases from Meat Consumption*, Santa Monica, CA: Leaves of Healing, 1979

Correct food-combining is one of the most important points dealt with in my books. According to research[118], a diet rich in proteins robs the body of its vital supply of pancreatic enzymes, which terminate healing processes, which can otherwise go on to form tumours if they are not arrested upon completion of their task.[119] These enzymes, such as trypsin and chymotrypsin, are employed as foreign proteins are broken down into their constituent amino acids and reconstructed as human proteins - a process extremely taxing on the body's resources.

We chomp meat because our society has bought into the fear of dying through lack of protein, most believing that unless we scarf down animal flesh by the rack-load, we are in serious danger of becoming protein-deficient. This myth originated from early trials conducted on rats. Later it transpired rats require up to *eleven times more protein than humans,* as evidenced by the commensurate increase in rat-mothers' proteins in milk, compared with the protein content of human milk.

Today, it is recognised that human protein requirements are not nearly as great as formerly thought (between 20 - 40 g/day). Yet many are ingesting 100 - 200 g/day. It is this excess that is causing all the bother - acidosis in the population that can eventually prove fatal. Nevertheless, the protein-scoffing trend has been hard to extirpate from the minds of the laity, whose stubbornness, as Dr Nelson states, has led to an abundance of sickness and disease in the protein-poisoned West.

The plain fact is, meat and dairy are not required by the body either for calcium, vitamins (apart from B9 & 12), minerals or

---

118 *Cancer Control Journal,* Vol. 6. No.1-6

119 **Binzel, P E** *Alive & Well,* American Media, 2000

proteins to maintain health and strength. In fact, in the case of calcium, meat can actually be a problem. Meat is generally high in phosphorous - an acid - which bonds with valuable alkalising calcium ions in the body to form apatite, which is then precipitated out of the body, causing a net calcium loss. The human body is not designed to consume human milk past infancy, nor is it designed for carnivorous meat intakes. Interestingly, all nutrients the human body requires may be obtained from the plant kingdom with no downside, save that of a recent mineral deficiency problem through over-farming.

This is not to say that a human *can't* eat some meat and dairy if they wish, let's just not have any of that rubbish about it being vital to the maintenance of human health. A small amount of organic meat is desirable for nutrients such as the B9 & B12 mentioned earlier, which are sometimes awkward to obtain for vegans, who run the risk of deficiencies if they are not diligent. A 5-10% component for organic meat/fish[120] and dairy, balanced with the remainder consisting of properly constituted whole-foods (salads, vegetables, nuts, legumes, etc.), seems to be ideal. Just be aware of the problems with heavy meat and dairy consumption and side-step them.

See *also:*
You Are What You Eat

---

[120] Fish is a great component for getting essential fatty acids (EFA's) into the body. Persons suffering from motor neuron diseases or 'mental illnesses' should increase their intakes of fish, minerals and fresh, clean water. Ensure the fish is of the deep-sea variety. Lightly broiled fish makes an ideal substitute for a lot of meats currently consumed in the Western diet. For a full treatment on mental illnesses, please see **Day, Phillip** *The Mind Game*, Credence, 2003

- 47 -
Avoid Vaccinations

'The whole aim of practical politics is to keep the populace alarmed - and hence clamorous to be led to safety - by menacing it with an endless series of hobgoblins, all of them imaginary.' - **H L Mencken**

'Even if we rapidly eliminate SARS, we remain at risk of future viral mutations, and should expect more dangerous new viruses to emerge over the next ten years.' **Dr Patrick Dixon, May 2003**

PLAGUE ATTACK *- The horrifying spectre of terrorists turning themselves into walking biological weapons on Britain's streets was raised by doctors. Fanatics could be given smallpox and walk amongst us infecting people, yet we only have a vaccine for one in three.* **Express Newspapers, 6th March 2003**

SMALLPOX KILLS! *Smallpox kills about 30% of those infected with the disease. There is no cure, but there is a vaccine. If given before exposure, the vaccine will prevent the disease from appearing. But is there enough for everyone?* **BBC NEWS, 13th January 2003**

TUBERCULOSIS! NEW SPECTRE OF THE WHITE DEATH *- We had it beaten, but TB is back and deadlier than ever.... Anyone who refuses inoculation is a danger both to society and to himself.* **Daily Mail, 30th March 2001**

MEASLES! *Public health officials have stressed the severity of the situation. The Government is now urging parents to take heed of this warning and allow their children to be immunised with* *the MMR jab before an epidemic sweeps the nation.* **Readers Digest, January 2001**

Another example of our faith in medical science - immunisation. Every autumn in England, hundreds of thousands line up at medical centres to get their flu jabs and other assorted cocktails. And guess what many of them get every year? The flu. Once again, we see two extremely polarised positions on a subject refusing to be reconciled - we're getting to know this pattern also.

The use of vaccines to prevent and eradicate scourges like smallpox and tuberculosis is supposedly one of the great successes of modern medicine. But much controversy has always surrounded vaccinations concerning the damage they can do to the immune system. With the fury felt by many of his day on the subject, Dr Herbert Shelton averred:

'This criminal practice will end as soon as parents develop sufficient interest in the welfare of their children. At present, parents offer up their children on the altars of the [vaccination] *goddess, because commercial ghouls demand it, and hope that the children will not be greatly injured. If a child is invalided for life or is killed, the parents meekly accept the lying excuses of the scoundrels who maim and murder children for money, cry a little, and return to their movies and joy rides.*

Reader, do you know how Judas felt after he had sold his master for a few pieces of silver? If you have surrendered your child to be vaccinated and inoculated after you learned the truth, you know how he felt. There is one great difference between you and him - Judas had decency enough to go out and hang himself.[121]

Whoa, Herbert!

These days, Dr Andrew Wakefield is feeling the heat. His research found measles virus in the bowels of autistic kids and the Establishment coughed up a hairball.

'Nobody has complained to the General Medical Council about Dr Andrew Wakefield,' Britain's *Daily Mail* thunders. *'Nobody has suggested that he said or wrote anything dishonest when he believed he had discovered a link between the MMR vaccine and autism. Yet the GMC has taken it upon itself to charge him with serious professional misconduct, threatening to strike him off, and, in doing so, destroy his livelihood. His research was 'inadequately founded', say the charges. He failed to obtain ethical committee approval before publishing, acquired funding improperly and subjected children to 'unnecessary and invasive investigations'. In short, the council is throwing the book at him. Why?*

The case has the whiff about it of a medieval inquisition, called to defend the orthodoxy of the establishment against the heresy of an independent mind.'[122]

Lucy Johnston writes: *'Four years ago, the Sunday Express revealed that at least 26 child deaths have been linked with the measles, mumps and rubella vaccine. In many cases, the*

---

[121] **Shelton, Herbert** *Vaccines and Serum Evils,* www.whale.to/vaccines/shelton1.html

[122] *Daily Mail,* 13th June 2006

government - or leading medical officials - accepted the connection.'[123]

In terms of income, there's no getting away from it, immunisation is the Big Kahuna. There's hardly an illness that does not scare the pants off the public to the extent they will sign on for any injection going. In some countries, your child must be vaccinated to enter the public school system. US levels of autism - a disease that apparently sprang from nowhere - have today reached unprecedented levels.

www.jabs.org.uk and www.vran.org are two websites set up for vaccine-damaged children and concerned parents, which push the case for urgent review. If immunisation is an issue with you, there's a chapter on vaccination in my book, *Health Wars,* and Steve Ransom does a fabulous job in his *Wake Up to Health in the 21st Century.*

See also:
Choose the Right Doctor
Admit When You're Wrong
Avoid Medical Testing Disease
Exercise Prevention
Take Responsibility For Your Actions

---

123 *Sunday Express,* 18th June 2006

~ 46 ~

Avoid Too Much Sun

'My parents warned me never to open the cellar door or I would see things I shouldn't see. So one day when they were out I did open the cellar door and I did see things I shouldn't see - grass, flowers, the sun....' - **Emo Phillips**

You need the sun.[124]

You don't need too much of it.[125]

Thus, another middle-of-the-roader.

First, let's lay a myth to rest. Sun does not cause skin cancer or everyone lounging in the sun would get skin cancer. Clearly, the sun can damage the skin if exposed excessively, giving rise to a healing process, which if it doesn't terminate, becomes cancer. This was the basis of Professor John Beard's thesis, published in 1904, an excerpt of which can be found in my B17 Metabolic Therapy manual. Australian schoolchildren being told the sun can give them skin cancer is unhelpful if they're not being advised at the same time to improve their nutrition and toss out the fizzy drinks and processed diets.

The body needs sunlight to make vitamins and replenish cells in a way we don't understand yet. Shut a plant in a cupboard and it dies. Yet we all know what happens when we get too much sun - skin types vary considerably in what they can absorb, from pale Celtic to black. Skin creams can be a problem too in that many

---

124 *Cancer,* March 2002; 94:1867-75

125 *Archives of Dermatology,* June 2002;138:771-774

contain chemicals which can react in sunlight to become carcinogens. Mike Adams from the 'Health Ranger' web-site:

'There are two primary reasons why sunscreen causes cancer. First, and most importantly, the use of sunscreen blocks the skin from absorbing the sun's rays. That's what it's supposed to do, right? Yes, but in doing so, it also blocks the creation of all-essential vitamin D, the nutrient that the human body desperately needs to prevent as many as 25 chronic diseases. Notably: prostate cancer, breast cancer, osteoporosis, schizophrenia and heart disease.

The second reason sunscreen causes cancer is because it contains toxic chemicals in the form of artificial fragrance, chemical colours and petroleum products used as fillers and stabilizers. These chemicals are absorbed through the skin where they enter the bloodstream and wreak havoc on the immune system. Artificial fragrances, just by themselves, may contain dozens of carcinogenic chemicals that damage the liver, the heart, and even promote systemic cancer.'[126]

Sunlight can actually prevent and help heal cancer, due to the Vitamin D element. Studies show there are 13 malignancies whose occurrences are inversely proportional to levels of D in the system.[127] Black races need up to 10 - 20 times the sun exposure than fairer-skinned people to make the Vitamin D levels to avoid cancer, which is thought to be the reason why African Americans in the US, especially those living in the north, have far higher levels of cancer than other ethnic groups.

---

[126] http://www.newstarget.com/001264.html

[127] *Cancer,* March 2002; 94:1867-75

Mercola reports that the prestigious National Academy of Sciences published a comprehensive review *'showing that the omega 6:3 ratio was the key to preventing skin cancer development. An Australian study done ten years ago showed a 40% reduction in melanoma for those who were eating fish. And this was without any attention to lowering omega-6 fats.*[128]

So sunlight can help with cancer, skin conditions, MS, depression and a whole host of other ailments so long as we don't burn. Combine a wise lifestyle with a healthy whole-food diet and tread those middle boards.

Tennis anyone?

See also:
Exercise – Walk 10,000 Steps a Day
Drink Two Litres of Water a Day
Eat Apricot Kernels Every Day
Breathe Clean Air
Take a Four-Week Holiday
Remove Toxins from Home and Work
Avoid Cancer
Get Enough Sleep
Attack Political Correctness
Exercise Prevention
There is Danger in Excess, Moderation in All Things

---

[128] http://www.mercola.com/2002/apr/3/sun_prevents_cancer.htm

~ 45 ~
Attack Political Correctness
A squirrel is just a rat with good public relations

The Week reports as follows:

'The University of California in Los Angeles has created 50 new courses since 11 September to 'explore the scope of issues emerging from the terrorist attacks'. In future, students will be able to study such topics as Navigating Between Blithesome Optimism and Cultural Despair, Women's Participation in Political Violence, and Understanding the Unthinkable and Incomprehensible.

Inmates of the Pascoe County jail in Florida complained that their new black and white striped uniforms, which replaced their orange outfits, were 'degrading'. "They make us look like convicts", said prisoner Shawn McCarthy.

The game of 'tag' has been outlawed in a school in the US because it violates the school's 'no touching' policy. A spokesman for the West Minneapolis education authority explained that children might not know the difference between 'good touches and bad touches'. "What we're trying to do," she explained, "is use structured discipline policies and logical consequences to let youngsters know what the rules are."'[129]

In 2002, CTM and Credence opened up research into the destructive effects of Outcome Based Education and a myriad of

[129] *The Week*, 22nd December 2001

psychiatrically driven initiatives designed to destroy the concept of right and wrong. One such area is the nonsensical system of social and professional control known as 'political correctness'. Most folk, of course, know the difference between right and wrong, but how many want to face the barrage of indignant ripostes from the minority and its media-driven liberal establishment, whose social experiments with education, drugs, pornography and Freud have wrought the havoc we see on our streets today?

Political correctness is a symptom of a sick society, of over-bloated government seeking work for an ever-expanding payroll. Under the guise of 'Health and Safety', these nazis roundly damn the right to free speech and self-expression for fear of offending minority elements. Mostly, the minority elements are as offended as the rest of us about it all.

To me, a politically-correct person is the real enemy. I may object to your views and you to mine, but I defend your right to the death to say what you want, where you want, when you want, because in a free society that's what free people can do. Imagine how potent free speech can be against an extremist minority seeking to impose their own unpopular world-view, who try to mine the trail behind them for fear of being ambushed. Well, ambushed they should be, at every river-crossing and on every dusty trail (they don't think I'm onto them but I am).

TEACHING RIGHT AND WRONG IS SCRAPPED, protests James Tozer in the Mail. *'Schools will no longer have to teach children the difference between right and wrong, it was revealed yesterday. The National Curriculum will be changed to say teachers merely have to help them develop 'secure values and beliefs'.*

And learning about Britain's cultural heritage will be dropped in favour of making sure pupils 'understand different cultures and traditions'.

There was anger and disbelief last night at the planned changes to the curriculum for 11 to 14-year-olds, which come at a time of growing concern about anti-social behaviour.'[130]

Did you know the organisers of the 200th anniversary of the Battle of Trafalgar were so desperate to avoid offending the French they had a blue fleet and a red fleet provided for the re-enactment of the battle?

Jimmy Cohen contacted the campaign Against Political Correctness to report how, on July 8th 2005, *'I decided to fly a British flag from my car due to my heartache and solidarity with the victims of the London bombings* ['7/7']. *The police pulled me over and told me that it could be considered racist and that I must take it down. Almost in tears I explained I was doing it for the people who were killed by the terrorists. The policeman just said that I had to take it down or he would arrest me for racial incitement.'*

Heather has a similar story: *'While living in Canada and working for Pottery Barn, we were told not to say 'Merry Christmas' but 'Happy Holidays'. I called a black board a black board and was told that I must never say this again as it is racially offensive. I was*

---

[130] *Daily Mail*, 31st July 2006, p.6

also told that I could not wear my cross because it might offend our Muslim workers. Did anyone think I might be offended? I think not.' [131]

Political correctness only survives due to the public's apathy to fight it. And the judiciary can't protest they are forced into these bizarre interpretations due to the European Convention on Human Rights, since the rest of Europe generally does what suits them - France especially. But good old Britain must do everything by the book, so dots the 'I's and crosses the 'T's and away we go into Wonderland; the 'bullied' city high-flier given £800,000 for her hurt feelings; Children not able to ride donkeys on Bognor Beach without wearing a full-face motorcycle crash helmet. Human rights lawyer, Cherie Blair.

Political correctness has emasculated the police, who these days in Britain are mostly to be found jailing pensioners for refusing to pay their Council Tax, arresting merchants for putting golliwogs in their shop windows, and rousting those who say unkind things against Paul Cahill's Gay Police Association.[132] Needless to say, while Plod has been otherwise occupied, crooks have been having a beano. British crime has soared as judgments are made in favour of the criminal. 'Life' for murder these days gets you eight years if that. School performance has plummeted, and don't even think about videotaping your child's Nativity play in case you're a paedophile.

Me? I don't happen to think Snow White is racially inappropriate, nor that the Seven Dwarfs are vertically challenged. Who on Earth will I offend next? Will 'innuendo'

---

131 *The Campaign Against Political Correctness* is at www.capc.co.uk

132 www.gay.police.uk

become an Italian suppository, or Little Red Riding Hood Vladimir Putin's contraceptive?

Politically correct weasels are the enemy and must be confronted at all costs. Tell 'em how mad you are, but use legal means, whatever that means these days. PC is minority extremism forced down ordinary people's throat and I've been choking for years, how about you? Eric Moir is worthy of the final word:

'My son is a music teacher,' he writes. *'When he started his first job, he was told he could not teach his pupils "Baa Baa Black Sheep", but had to use 'Baa Baa HAPPY Sheep instead.'*[133]

Oh, God.

I mean -

See also:
Don't Lose Your Joy
Manage Your Anger
Own a Good Conscience
There is Danger in Excess, Moderation in All Things
Obtain Control Over Your Sense of Certainty
Don't Break the Law
Avoid Dreamkillers
Guard Input
Start Complaining
Be Polite (But Don't Be Walked Over)
Help Others

---

[133] http://www.capc.co.uk/stories.htm

- 44 -
Work at Self-Improvement

'I cannot believe out of 100,000 sperm, you were the quickest.' - **Steven Pearl**

Working at self-improvement is less élitist and prideful than a safety mechanism to avoid falling into bad habits. Deciding on what standards and values you'll subscribe to gives you your margin of operation to work within.

- So you're gaining weight. How heavy will you get before you do something about it?
- Do you share the same values as your spouse or partner?
- Are there things about you that need changing?
- Are you going to do anything about them?
- Do you know how to do anything about them?

Sometimes a nudge is all it takes for someone to admit, *'Yeah, I've been putting it off. I need to do something about my smoking, drinking, drugs, diet, foul mouth...'* Working at self-improvement is also the recognition that we'll never have the perfect body, fortune, wit or charisma, but we are a work in motion, and by keeping the leash taught and maintaining standards, we can avoid getting hurt and be better equipped for the tough times, and you know they'll come calling.

What You Can Do

- If I am unhappy with my life, <u>I</u> can do something about it
- <u>I</u> can take action
- I will only take action if I am uncomfortable enough

- When I am uncomfortable or motivated enough, I gain leverage
- Gaining leverage is when I am compelled to act *immediately* and *irresistibly*
- To take action I must decide where I want to go
- Setting goals gives me a course of action
- Now I can plan the steps to carry out my mission
- Each step must impress me enough to move on to the next
- My goals must be irresistible, impress the heck out of me
- I must take action if I want a result
- To achieve my goals, *I must really want them*
- I can improve my well-being by increasing placebic effects in my life (the positive), and decreasing nocebos (the negative)
- I can steer my own destiny
- *I can really do this!*

In fact, ***NEXT!***

See also:

You're Never Too Old to Change
Set Goals Daily
Be an Overcomer
Get Out of Debt
Think Good Thoughts, Don't Dwell on Evil
Simplify, Simplify, Simplify
Never Retire
Strive for Excellence
Laugh a Lot
Deal With Chronic Issues
Listen to What Comes Out of Your Mouth
Turn Off the TV
Create Overwhelming Optimistic Experiences

Reward Yourself
Own a Good Conscience
Obtain Control Over Your Sense of Certainty
Be Inspired
Experience Success
Take Responsibility For Your Actions
Be Disciplined
Be Thankful
Help Others
Have A Point to It All

- 43 -
Create Overwhelming Optimistic Experiences

The scientific theory I like best is that the rings of Saturn are composed entirely of lost airline luggage.' - **Mark Russell**

We looked at goal-setting earlier, but creating overwhelming optimistic experiences is not only the key to broadening your outlook and pleasure, but also serves the very real purpose of bribing you into doing those things you would rather avoid.

Each morning when you wake up, plan at least one overwhelming optimistic experience for the day. They do not have to be 'mighty' events, they do have to overwhelm you with enjoyment and genuinely monopolise your interest. If you think about it, having to find at least one a day for the next thirty days is going to compel you to think seriously about your enjoyment. Good, since we tend to spend the majority of our brain-time devising new and interesting ways to wind ourselves up.

Overwhelming optimistic experiences are R & R down-time, so *don't* stress out about them! Start a new hobby. Go swimming in the sea. See a film or play. Visit an area of outstanding natural beauty. Play paintball. Learn a new skill. Ride a horse. Eat out at a restaurant with friends in lovely surroundings. Take a balloon ride. Visit someone you like whom you haven't seen for a while. Visit the zoo. Sit down with the book you've wanted to read for a long time. Learn a new skill. The possibilities are endless.

Changing States

Understanding the power behind overwhelming optimistic experiences is to understand the state change. While we are alive we experience *states* - emotional conditions that determine our mood or outlook. Coffee, tea and stimulants such as sugar, drugs and adrenalin highs are all used to achieve *state changes* from perceived pain to perceived pleasure. These are never long-lasting, and the resultant *loss of any state we gain* vexes us, since what caused the pain in first place hasn't been resolved. We experience a negative shift in mood so we seek to regain a new high with another state change – the classic addiction profile.

What everyone ultimately strives for is a *state*. An emotion. Physical possessions are one means of achieving these states, though notice a difference. Ask any fifteen-year-old girl in the Western world what, out of all the things on Earth, she would most like to have, and some might say *"Brad Pitt!"* And yet Brad, like all humans, is nothing but several yards of intestines, a squashy brain, lots of gooey red stuff and all the vices common to the human condition. What the girl wants is the *state* she believes she will experience from owning Brad Pitt. The satisfying feeling of jealous girlfriends, a beautiful man and the social status among her peers of being seen with one of the most unavailable but desirable bipeds on the planet.

A seventeen-year-old male will probably want a Ferrari. But notice that a Ferrari is nothing but metal, glass, rubber, smelly oil and a bunch of electrical wiring. This boy wants what he believes the Ferrari will do for him. He is striving for an ultimate *state.*

We are satisfied when we achieve a state that brings us balance and equilibrium. Think of the days when the sun is shining and all's well with the world. Anthony Robbins tells us there are several ways to force a state change without resorting to shopping, chemicals or food. The first is to alter your body language. Those who are depressed have body language which suits depression. If you are depressed, practise straightening your body and pacing around the room with a sense of purpose. Fix yourself in the mirror with that irresistible smile. If you change your body language, your emotional state will invariably move in the same direction if you are consistent.

Changing your attitude, or angle of attack, is the second method. This is altering your mental body language and has the same effect as the point above. Removing negative stimuli from your life, such as TV, newspapers, gloomy friends and other baleful influences, will cause a state change all on its own. Overwhelming experiences are all about state changes. While choosing an activity, concentrate on the following:

- Go for *your own* maximum personal enjoyment, not someone else's, though enjoying yourself can mean helping someone else
- Your overwhelming optimistic experience *doesn't have to mean anything or have a purpose* other than to give you great pleasure, so don't get wound up about it!
- It's OK to repeat an activity, but varying your experiences will maximise the effect. Think how much ground you can cover in thirty days

If you need inspiration, once again take a trip to the bookstore and see what everyone else is doing. As mentioned in *The Little Book of Attitude*, If I find myself with time on my hands, I visit Barnes and Noble or Waterstones to trawl through the books. Running a business, cooking, the military, space exploration, football, embroidery, love stories, working with animals. The point is, stimulate *your* interest and think about taking *yourself* in a completely new direction. See how it suits *you*.

See also:

You're Never Too Old to Change
Set Goals Daily
Put Plants Around the Place
Get a Hobby
Get a Pet
Think Good Thoughts, Don't Dwell on Evil
Live in the Present
Breathe Clean Air
See the World and Have No Fear
Take a Four-Week Holiday
Turn Off the TV
Be In Love
Reward Yourself
Dare to Dream
Be Inspired

~ 42 ~
Eat Garlic

Almost all cultures in the world use garlic. Not all cultures in the world know that garlic is Nature's most potent antibiotic and a lot more besides. Peter Josling does, he's studied the stuff for years at Britain's Garlic Centre and his book, *Allicin – The Heart of Garlic*, is the first popular, comprehensive outing by a scientist on the benefits of this most marvellous of extracts.

'Garlic contains many beneficial components,' he writes, *'and over the last 10 to 15 years an enormous amount of research has been published on the properties of various breakdown components that are formed when fresh garlic is cut, crushed, chopped or processed. Of these well-known and categorized sulphur-containing chemicals, it is allicin that stands out head and shoulders above the rest, showing the most exciting, interesting and beneficial properties.*

Now, with the advent of new technology, for the first time ever it is possible to produce stabilized allicin on a commercial scale. This has led to research confirming the most incredible spectrum of activity against today's most pressing problems – resistant bacteria, viral and fungal infections, and micro-organisms that have long been the scourge of modern man.'[134]

There are a few who cannot stand garlic, and for them, Nature has an arsenal of other substances listed in *The ABC's of Disease*

---

[134] **Josling, Peter** *Allicin – The Heart of Garlic,* NWI Publishing, 2004. Available though www.credence.org

(*see* 'Anti-*Candida*/Fungal Supplementation'). For the rest, garlic/allicin represents a highly potent, holistic way to:

- Boost the immune system
- Fight yeast and fungal overgrowths
- Kill parasites and viruses

Allicin is a proven weapon in the fight against disease. Josling and others have published a plethora of research showing allicin demonstrates significant efficacy in treating the problems below. It is in its role as a cold preventative, however, that garlic, to-date, has been most well-known.[135]

Acne, AIDS, animal bites, arthritis, asthma, athlete's foot, bacterial infections, bad breath(!), bladder infections, blood pressure, boils, candidiasis, canker sores, cellulitis, cholesterol control, circulation, cold sores, colds and influenza, coughs and respiratory infections, cryptosporidium poisoning, dandruff, diabetes, diaper (nappy) rash, diarrhoea, delayed aging, ear infections, eye infections, ebola and dengue fever, eczema, fungal nail disease, gingivitis, hay fever, heavy metal contamination, hepatitis, immune system irregularities, impetigo, impotence, irritable bowel syndrome, mosquitoes, MRSA infection, parasites, peptic ulcer, pre-eclampsia in pregnancy, protozoal infections, psoriasis, ringworm, rosacea, shingles, sinusitis, sore throat, thrush, toothache, traveller's tum, TB, verrucae, viral infections, warts, wounds, vampires –

Don't be without this indispensable aid.[136]

---

135 Adv Therapy, 'Preventing the common cold with a garlic supplement: a double-blind, placebo-controlled survey', 2001 Jul-Aug;18(4):189-93.

136 Allicin capsules and sprays are available from the Credence Store

- 41 -
Manage Your Anger

'Go, and never darken my towels again!' - **Groucho Marx**

Anger is not the event itself but your interpretation of it.

After you've calmed down, was your anger *reasonable?*

- Always seek a peaceful resolution to a conflict
- Don't deliberately make trouble for someone
- If someone is determined to make trouble for you, execute a *proportionate* response to the threat coming against you
- If necessary, have a third party mediate

That Gets My Goat

Are you short-fused for no good reason? Most attitude problems, such as 'mental illness', anger, stress, road rage, etc. derive from the hamster wheel spinning too fast. Once again, stop reading newspapers, eat plenty of fresh whole-foods (including those omega 3's), exercise, and get out of town for a four-week break to calm yourself down.

By far the greatest problems with anger are lifestyle and diet-related.[137] Many of the popular psychiatric drugs manipulate levels of serotonin, the mood molecule, to cure symptoms, so once again the underlying problem remains unresolved. I am not against anger as a social statement - maturely directed, it can get things done. I

(www.credence.org) for most countries

137 **Day, Phillip** *The Mind Game,* Credence, 2003. A summary of this can be found in my book, *The ABC's of Disease,* under various 'disease' headings

founded the Campaign For Truth In Medicine because of my resentment (anger) at the quackery being practised by the establishment for profit. Yet I don't intend beating any of these people up or emptying their garbage all over their front lawn.

Many whip up their social indignation reading the newspapers every day, realising at the same time there's precious little they can do about it. This emotional impotence is simply no good for the old ticker. Each of us must decide how much extraneous influence and junk we want to allow to pressure our lives. It is sobering that if you didn't watch the news or read newspapers, you'd hardly be aware, much less affected by the following, which may have been a cause of anger for you in the past:

- 9/11 (Twin Towers and Washington attacks)
- 7/11 (London bombings)
- The Afghan War
- The Iraq War (parts 1, 2 and 'the peace')
- Israel, Palestine and the Gaza Strip
- Tony Blair, John Prescott, Bush, Cheney, Rumsfeld et al
- Bird flu, swine flu, Hong Kong flu, SARS, AIDS, etc
- The Eurovision Song Contest
- Minority immigrant/asylum/crime/gay and lesbian policy
- Global warming
- The Indonesian tsunami, Hurricane Andrew, etc
- Earthquakes around the world and other natural disasters

The point being made here is, don't emotionally bite off more than you can chew. Over-stimulation of the senses via media is one of the most devastating yet rarely discussed nocebos of our modern culture. And then there's Red Bull.

See also:

You're Never Too Old to Change
The Sky Rarely Falls In
Be an Overcomer
You Are What You Eat
Exercise - Walk 10,000 Steps a Day
Lose the Mobile Phone
Think Good Thoughts, Don't Dwell on Evil
Admit When You're Wrong
Laugh a Lot
Listen to What Comes Out of Your Mouth
Turn Off the TV
Avoid Psychiatrists
Don't Lose Your Joy
Attack Political Correctness
Reduce or Eliminate Red Meat
Don't Break the Law
Guard Input
Start Complaining
Be Thankful

- 40 -
Avoid Medical Testing Disease

If you think you're completely healthy, you've simply not had enough tests yet

Today the medical testing industry rides high on the gullibility of the public, doling out everything from mammograms to cholesterol tests, thyroid to blood sugar readings. Most still believe doctor knows best and if he calls us in because we're overdue for a test, then grab your scarf, Mabel, the wind's got a chill in it this morning.

This is another of those times when the middle course must be steered - alas, all too many of us are hopeless at it. Rarely do we question the experts, when we could, or hold them to account, which we should. I have come across the same baleful establishment attitude in many countries, which can only be described as a deep, overriding contempt for the public - a public hectored, bullied and coerced into compliance and treated like naughty schoolchildren. Millions today drug up their kids on the basis of fraudulent 'diagnoses' like ADD, OCD and schizophrenia, assuming the 'experts' know what they're talking about. They don't. Millions more are talked into taking statins for non-existent heart conditions, warfarin (rat poison) for chunky blood that could be thinned out as easily by diet and exercise, and genetic tests so women can have their healthy breasts lopped off to save them getting breast cancer. *This is progress?*

Snake oil takes on a new look when you examine how drugs and tests are marketed today. Most newspapers in Britain have a health section once a week comprising 8-10 pages of stories which are nothing more than thinly-veiled drug advertorials. Remember the postcode lottery scam for Herceptin? Everyone panicked they weren't going to get this breast cancer 'wonder-drug' because they lived in the wrong area. Notice that in all the hype and kafuffle, rarely was it discussed whether the drug *actually worked at all,* and more poignantly, its safety record:

Breast Cancer Drug Blamed For Deaths: *Genentech Inc. mailed a letter to doctors Thursday warning that the breast cancer drug Herceptin has been linked to 15 deaths and 47 other adverse reactions in patients. In nine of the 15 deaths, symptoms arose within 24 hours after Herceptin was administered, according to the letter. Genentech is working with the FDA to have the drug's label amended to reflect the new risks.*[138]

What, something like *'Warning. Can cause symptoms leading to death within 24 hours'?*

After seeing the toe-curling performance of our medical peers in the fall-out over Wakefield's research on MMR, nothing short of an 'Elephant Man' drug-trial disaster gets anyone close to admitting a problem. And in the latter's case, no-one was eventually blamed for what happened to those 'guinea-pigs', who have since been advised most will probably contract cancer.[139] In fact, one of them already has.[140]

11th - 13th April 2006 saw an interesting event occur in Newcastle, Australia: The Inaugural Conference on Disease-Mongering: *'Everyone who attended the conference learned*

---

138 "Breast cancer drug blamed for deaths", *USA Today,* 5th May 2000

139 *Daily Mail,* 31st July 2006, p.11

140 *Daily Express,* 7th August 2006

something new. We learned that the techniques of 'disease-mongering', in particular the expansion of the boundaries of disorders, the medicalisation of normal life events and the portrayal of risk factors as diseases are prevalent in the medical marketing world today.'[141]

The British Medical Journal also discusses disease-mongering: *'There's a lot of money to be made from telling healthy people they're sick. Some forms of medicalising ordinary life may now be better described as disease-mongering: widening the boundaries of treatable illness in order to expand markets for those who sell and deliver treatments. Pharmaceutical companies are actively involved in sponsoring the definition of diseases and promoting them to both prescribers and consumers. The social construction of illness is being replaced by the corporate construction of disease.'* [142]

Mammograms

Peter Gotzsche of the Nordic Cochrane Centre in Copenhagen, writes: *'In some countries, women are invited for mammography in a letter in which the date and time of the appointment have already been fixed. This puts pressure on these women, who must actively decline the invitation if they don't want to be screened.*

Sometimes, women are asked to give reasons for not attending appointments, as if it were a civic duty. In leaflets, women get simple messages — that cancer detected early can be cured, and early cancers can often be treated with breast-conserving surgery. The data tell another story: no reliable evidence shows

---

[141] www.diseasemongering.org

[142] http://bmj.bmjjournals.com/cgi/content/full/324/7342/886#B1#B1;

breast screening saves lives; breast screening leads to more surgery, including more mastectomies; and estimates show that more than a tenth of healthy women who attend a breast screening programme experience considerable psychological distress for many months.'[143]

Mammograms can cause breast cancer - official.[144] Though, if you think about it, persuading millions of women to slam their breasts in a cold fridge door and irradiate them with over one thousand times the rads of a chest x-ray would seem a trifle contrived if you were attempting to rip off the public. The irony is, those sincere, well-meaning souls who schedule you for your prostate test or mammogram have all the best intentions, much like the disabled guy collecting for cancer at the motorway service area.

Dr John McDougall points out that the $5-13 billion per year generated by mammograms controls the information women get. Fear and incomplete data are the tools commonly used to persuade women to get routine mammograms. Says Dr McDougall:

'I went into medicine with the idea that I was going to save all of these lives with all the tricks and tools that medical doctors learned. And what I found was that very few of my patients got well. I often did harm to them. This was quite disturbing to me as a young doctor. What was even more disturbing was to find out that this failure had been fairly well documented in the scientific literature - but it doesn't fit anybody's advertising campaign.

---

143 http://bmj.bmjjournals.com/cgi/content/full/324/7342/886#resp1

144 Daily Mail, 'Mammograms Can Increase Breast cancer Risk,' 27th June 2006

Science says one thing and the public believes another because the public relations machine benefits the economics of the drug and medical industries. Mammography is a fraud. The 8th January 2000 issue of the Lancet carried an article stating that mammography is unjustifiable. Of the eight studies done, six of them show that mammography doesn't work, and yet the American public believes this is a time-honoured, definite way of saving their lives from breast cancer.'[145]

Safe Alternatives

A non-invasive, non-radiation alternative to mammography is Digital Thermal Imaging (DTI)[146], or alternatively, breast self-examination.[147] What other tests are you being lined up for that could be avoided, along with the corresponding mental anguish? Did you know that menopause is not a disease, irritable bowel syndrome can be caused by digestive upsets, and ADD/ADHD is mostly badly-fed kids capping off because they're not forming prostaglandins?[148]

Don't be conned.

Be wise and ask questions.

Tread the middle course.

---

[145] An Interview with Dr John McDougall: www.shareguide.com/McDougall.html

[146] www.meditherm.com

[147] For more on this subject, see **Ransom, Steven** *Great News on Cancer in the 21st Century*, Credence, 2004

[148] **Day, Phillip** *The ABC's of Disease*, Credence, 2003

- 39 -
Use Himalayan Salt

'Your table salt is actually 97.5% sodium chloride and 2.5% chemicals such as moisture absorbents and iodine. Dried at over 1,200 degrees Fahrenheit, the excessive heat alters the natural chemical structure of the salt causing the potential for a myriad of health problems in your body.' - **Dr Joseph Mercola**

Common table salt is a poison, refined from Nature's storehouse to remove all elements but sodium chloride. Some say we ended up with this particular compound due to industry's colossal use of it. Whatever the reason, table salt is not real 'salt' as it should be and its dangers are well touted:

- It destabilises blood pressure
- Can cause cellulite, kidney stones and rheumatism
- Upsets your fluid balance
- Acts as a diuretic (expels water from cells)
- Thereby a cell-toxin
- Contains the endocrine disrupters, fluoride and iodine
- Contains fillers such as calcium carbonate and aluminium hydroxide, the latter aluminium implicated in Alzheimer's Disease

Some PR job to convince the world we need it, eh?

Yet 'salt' is essential for the body's systems. Farmers know if they don't put out the salt blocks for their cattle, they die. This is real salt as Nature intended, not the truncated, worse-than-useless mess made of it in the refining process.

Enter saltpan salt, sea salt, Celtic salt, and the pink Dalek of all salts, Himalayan crystallized salt, or 'white gold' as it's come to be known (light pink gold, actually). Mercola declares this mother-of-all-salts:

- *Regulates the water content throughout your body*
- *Balances excess acidity from your cells, particularly your brain cells*
- *Balances your blood sugar levels and helps reduce your aging rate*
- *Assists in the generation of hydroelectric energy in cells in your body and absorption of food particles through your intestinal tract*
- *Helps clear mucus plugs and phlegm from your lungs - particularly useful in asthma and cystic fibrosis*
- *Acts as a strong natural antihistamine to help clear up congestion in your sinuses*
- *Prevents muscle cramps*
- *Makes the structure of your bones firm - osteoporosis can occur when your body needs more salt and takes it from your bones*
- *Regulates your sleep - it is a natural hypnotic*
- *Maintains your libido*
- *Prevents varicose veins and spider veins on your legs and thighs*
- *Stabilizes irregular heartbeats - in conjunction with water,* [salt] *is actually essential for the regulation of your blood pressure*

These claims are backed by evidence. Barbara Hendel MD and Peter Ferreira cover most of it in *Water and Salt, The Essence of Life* (available through Amazon). World renowned water guru, Dr

Fereydoon Batmanghelidj's *Water and Salt, Your Healers From Within,* available through Credence, contains much of the Iranian physician's decades of studies into the building blocks of life. The manufacturers of FIJI water, as another example, remark on their web-site:

'A nine-week, double-blind university study undertaken in 2003 at the Inter-University of Graz, Austria, examined the effects of drinking a minimum of 1.5 liters of tap water per day with common table salt vs. a minimum of 1.5 liters of FIJI Water with Original Himalayan Crystal Salt on physical and psychological functions of the body. In the study, patients who drank FIJI Water together with the Original Himalayan Crystal Salt saw significant positive changes in respiratory, circulatory, organ, connective tissue and nervous system functions. Patients also reported increases in the quality of sleep, energy and concentration levels, brain activity, weight loss, enhanced consciousness and noticeable nail and hair growth.'[149]

The medical orthodoxy is not kind to any notion of a super-salt, crying 'commercialism' and 'quackery', indubitably the pot calling the kettle black. My advice? Switch to Himalayan salt or at least a whole salt. Table salt is just that - sodium chloride. Himalayan salt is sodium chloride plus 82 other minerals in its natural, crystalline form, all ready to feed metabolic processes the way Nature intended. There are other advantages.

---

149 http://www.himalayancrystalsalt.com/html/research.html

Get Sole And Slap it All Over

Topical applications and baths in whole salt solutions have been found to help with psoriasis, eczema, toe-nail fungus, insect bites, rheumatism and arthritis, acne, ear infections, nasal congestion and sore throats. This solution used is known as *sole,* (pronounced *so-lay*). Take a container of water and start mixing Himalayan salt crystals into it, stirring well, until the salt no longer dissolves. The solution is now 26% saturated and sterile, so can be re-used. Sole in a hot water bowl can be inhaled as a decongestant for blocked sinuses since it is antiseptic and ideal for bacterial/fungal/yeast conditions.

See also:
You Are What You Eat
Get in the Raw
Exercise - Walk 10,000 Steps a Day
Limit Caffeine, Alcohol and Carbonated Drinks
Drink Two Litres of Water a Day
Reduce or Eliminate Red Meat
There is Danger in Excess, Moderation in All Things

Books available through www.credence.org:
Water and Salt, Your Healers From Within

~ 38 ~
Consider a Bowel Cleanse

*'Sir, I suggest your motives here
are totally intestinal!'* – **toilet graffiti**

'Most people who eat the standard American 'goo and glue' diet have about 5-10 pounds of matter stored in the colon.' – ***USA Today*, 11th January 1999**

'Of all the polite topics of conversation, the state of one's intestines is probably at the bottom of most people's lists. Let's face it: Irritable bowel syndrome, constipation, gas, diverticulitis and colon cancer are simply not things we like to discuss. And yet, as the old expression goes, death begins in the colon. Don't believe it? Ask any coroner. Autopsies often reveal colons that are plugged up to 80 percent with waste material.' – ***Vegetarian Times*, March 1998**

'Through my 25 years in medical practice and healthcare... I have come to believe that the cleansing/detoxification process is the missing link in Western nutrition and one of the keys to real healing. I have seen hundreds of patients over the years transform regular or persistent illness into health and greatly improved vitality.' – **Elson M. Haas, MD**

During the years I have reported on health issues, I've spoken with literally hundreds of doctors around the world. One of the most common statements they make? *The key to long-term health is a clean, well-functioning digestive system.* Of course, with our drug-predominant medical culture, neglect of the basics is virtually assured:

Optimum Nutrition - *Real food*
Optimum Hydration - *Real water*
Optimum Absorption - *A clean, well functioning digestive system*
Optimum Assimilation - *Adequate vitamins, minerals, etc.*
Optimum Elimination - *Regular, efficient bowel movements*

These five make up the metabolic processes by which the body replenishes itself with nutrients, repairs damage, bolsters immunity and eliminates waste. At the heart of this wondrous creation is the digestive system, whose chronic problems can bear grave ramifications for every organ of the body:

STOMACH AND BOWEL CANCER
CROHN'S DISEASE (REGIONAL ENTERITIS)
ULCERATIVE COLITIS
LEAKY GUT SYNDROME
DIVERTICULOSIS, DIVERTICULITIS
DYSBIOSIS
IRRITABLE BOWEL SYNDROME (IBS)
COELIAC DISEASE
CHRONIC CONSTIPATION

Chief Causes of Digestive Diseases

- Gluten/gliaden damage from wheat, barley, rye and oat products
- Bacterial and/or mycoplasmic (fungal) infections
- Small intestine bacterial overgrowths (SIBOs), brought on by low digestive enzyme output and excess histamine
- Processed diets

- Too much refined sugar and grains (a high percentage of western grains, stored in silos, are contaminated with *aspergillus* moulds)
- Too little fibre
- Clogged or damaged villi receptors in the intestine preventing adequate nutrient absorption
- A generally acidic, anaerobic internal environment, resulting in an inadequate immune system response
- Antibiotic abuse
- General drug abuse
- Poor water intake

In her best-selling book, *Internal Cleansing*, Dr Linda Berry, a chiropractor and clinical nutritionist, summarises the symptoms of self-poisoning as follows:

'If you experience any of the following symptoms, you may be experiencing autointoxication (a process whereby you are poisoned by substances produced by your own body as a result of inadequate digestion and elimination), and therefore you might want to consider some type of internal cleansing program:

- *Allergy or intolerance to certain foods*
- *Bad breath and foul-smelling gas and stools*
- *Constipation, diarrhoea, sluggish elimination, irregular bowel movements*
- *Frequent congestion, colds, viruses*
- *Flatulence or gas and frequent intestinal disorders*
- *Frequent headaches for no apparent reason*
- *General aches and pains that migrate from one place to another*
- *Intolerance to fatty foods*

- *Low energy; loss of vitality for no apparent reason*
- *Lower back pain*
- *Lowered resistance to infections*
- *Needing to sleep a long time*
- *Pain in your liver or gall bladder*
- *Premenstrual syndrome (PMS), breast soreness, vaginal infections*
- *Skin problems, rashes, boils, pimples, acne*

Candida Albicans

... a usually benign and beneficial bowel yeast, can also be a troublemaker. When fed a constant diet of its favourite totty, glucose (derived not only from sucrose, but from bread, potatoes, sweets, alcohol, rice, etc.) and housed in its ideal environment of acidic, oxygen-repelling, fermentation-rich tissues and ductal structures, it multiplies prolifically and can damage healthy cells, producing toxins that compromise the body's own immune defences in conditions such as 'candidiasis', sometimes referred to as 'the yeast syndrome'.

Gary Carlsen, of the US Candida Wellness Center, told me in Denver: *'The majority who have Candida do not realise they have it until they become seriously ill. The symptoms are so numerous and seemingly unrelated that it is very perplexing to both doctor and patient. Candida albicans is an incredible destroyer of health and is the missing link in understanding many of our modern-day diseases and poor health conditions. Candida robs the body of its nutrition and poisons the tissues with its toxins.'*

Those suffering from candidiasis may have a history of use of antibiotics, prednisone or other cortisone-type drugs. They are bothered by tobacco smoke and perfumes. They can feel spacey or 'not quite there', variously suffering menstrual irregularities, endometriosis, spots in front of eyes, diarrhoea, constipation, chaotic bowel movements, muscle aches and prostatitis.

Associated Complaints

Irritable bowel syndrome, eczema, psoriasis, depression, irritability, pre-menstrual syndrome (PMS), cancer, multiple sclerosis, heart disease, arthritis, osteoporosis, chronic fatigue syndrome (ME), leaky gut syndrome, oesophageal reflux, lupus, gout, Crohn's disease, hyperactivity, infertility, herpes, chlamydia, Alzheimer's, scleroderma, Raynaud's disease, kidney stones, Cushing's disease.

Causes of *Candida* Overgrowths

Parasites, yeast, fungi and bacteria invariably proliferate in moist, warm zones, especially when beneficial gut flora are killed by:

- Antibiotics and other drugs
- Malnutrition
- Constant cooked food devoid of enzymes
- An acidic diet [150]
- Cigarette smoking
- Fluoridated and chlorinated water consumption
- Antacids
- Excess sugar and high-glycaemic carbohydrate intake

Detoxifying the digestive tract and replenishing the intestinal micro-flora can help:

---

150 See **Day, Phillip** *Food For Thought*, Credence, 2003 - the official recipe companion to all Credence health titles

- Prevent illness
- Improve your physical appearance
- Control or eliminate yeast overgrowths
- Boost your emotional well-being
- Sharpen your mental capabilities
- Give you better, more complete digestion
- Eliminate unhealthy food addictions & allergies
- Help reduce or attain your ideal body weight
- Help reduce the effects of ageing

Dr Bernard Jensen, D.C., Ph.D., a world-renowned author of many popular health books, states: *'In the 50 years I've spent helping people to overcome illness, disability and disease, it has become crystal clear that poor bowel management lies at the root of most people's health problems. In treating over 300,000 patients, it is the bowel that invariably has to be cared for first before any effective healing can take place.'*

If you would like a simple program to cleanse and revitalise the bowel, obtain a copy of my booklet, *Digestive Heath.*[151] The goal is to help kill parasites and fungal/yeast infections, clear out the bowel, and replenish with healthy probiotics, the beneficial beasties which restore digestive balance. The program lasts one month, with the active, flushing phase during the first two weeks.

---

[151] **Day, Phillip** *Digestive Health,* Credence 2005

- 37 -
Reward Yourself

Do you like yourself?

How can you tell?

Do you hurt yourself?

Habits such as overeating, smoking, bulimia, nail-biting, self-harm, etc., are clues to a self-image problem which has been installed through Pavlov patterning (repetition). Changing how we view ourselves is like anything else, it requires consistency and practice to establish the new behaviour.

Go somewhere nice to stimulate your senses - a park, a beach, a forest or lake. Reward yourself, not with chocolate fudge brownies but with elements you know your body will thrive on: fresh air, fresh food, fresh water, exercise, happiness and hope.

Rewarding Yourself is about your relationship with you. Try being more gentle. If you self-hound, you old dog, ease back on the leash and try trotting a while. Spend time with yourself in the absence of extraneous input. Be calm, you are exactly where you need to be. This is the day that has been appointed to you. Celebrate it.

See also:
Create Overwhelming Optimistic Experiences
Take a Four-Week Holiday
The Sky Rarely Falls In

~ 36 ~

Give Yourself Permission to Recover

'As a man thinks in his heart, so is he.' – **Proverbs 23:7**

Vital to recovering from any illness is sending the unequivocal message to your cells that you are on the road to recovery. The placebic effect is the mind-body connection, which acutely affects immune function. When we are doom-laden (nocebo-influenced), immune function is suppressed. When we are optimistic and hopeful (placebo-influenced), the opposite occurs.

Today's science of psychoneuroimmunology (PNI) seeks to unravel the complex interaction between our thoughts and the body's interpretation of them. Many conventional scientists are excited by the potential of this approach, though the technique and its myriad applications are anything but new.

'As a scientist... I want to see hard, scientific proof before I commit to saying that something can work,' writes Professor Kathy Sykes. *'...But I have to concede that* [my BBC 2] *series opened my eyes and made me rethink some of my attitudes. I watched, for example, a young lady having open-heart surgery in China with only the use of acupuncture with some local anaesthetic as pain relief. She was completely conscious as her sternum was cracked open and a hole in her heart sewn up, without showing any discomfort - there could be no faking that...*

In one incredible segment, I visited Dr Bruce Moseley, a knee surgeon in the US, who carried out an experiment on patients with damaged patellas - knee caps. With one set of patients he carried out the conventional operation - he cut the knee open, scraped away the debris from the worn-out patella and sewed it back up. With the control group, however, he cut the knee open and then sewed it back up without removing the debris.

Amazingly, the control group - who were unaware they had been selected - reported recovery of the use of the knee at exactly the same rate as those who had undergone the conventional surgery and, five years on, the knee was still performing well.'[152]

This idea of consistent optimism extends beyond matters medical. As Anthony Robbins and Deepak Chopra exhaustively demonstrate, financial problems, relationship issues and professional challenges can all be influenced by consistent, positive action.[153] In other words:

- I can do this
- I'm going to feel better
- I'll reorganize my day to reflect my recovery
- I'll change my body language accordingly
- This problem is not even an issue for me anymore

See also:
Set Goals Daily
Be an Overcomer
Choose the Right Doctor
The Sky Rarely Falls In
Think Good Thoughts, Don't Dwell on Evil
Laugh a Lot
Obtain Control Over Your Sense of Certainty

---

[152] www.dailymail.co.uk, search under 'Kathy Sykes'

[153] ww.anthonyrobbins.com; www.chopra.com

~ 35 ~
Juice Veggies

Don't juice fruits (too much acid and sugar), *juice veggies.* [154]

A juicer is your secret weapon for good health and longevity. By juicing a selection of vegetables each day, you can dramatically increase your intake of natural enzymes and antioxidants, which arrest the ageing process and prevent against disease. Author Maria Costantino says:

'We know we should eat five portions of fruits and vegetables a day but most of us don't. Instead, we undermine the value of our food by eating too much of the wrong kinds and too little of the right kinds. In the USA, for example, the average adult manages just one and a half portions of fruits and vegetables a day, while in Britain, a remarkable 65% of the population eat only one portion. No wonder we moan about being tired, run down, sick and lacking in 'joie de vivre'.' [155]

Vegetable juices assist in alkalising the body, which in turn floods the body with oxygen.[156] Organic green veggies, in particular, are loaded with chlorophyll, iron, the correct (fine) calcium, and numerous vitamins, minerals and amino acids. Remember, greens are what turn baby gorillas into big ones. They also turn big gorillas in the classroom into meeker, more

---

[154] Fruit, consumed sparingly in its whole-food form, assists the body towards an alkaline state. Concentrated fruit juice is acidic. Rule of thumb: *Don't drink more of the juice than you would eat of the fruit.*

[155] **Costantino, Maria** *The Handbook of Energy Drinks,* Silverdale Books, 2004

[156] Day, Phillip, *Cancer: Why We're Still Dying to Know the Truth,* op. cit.

subservient versions of their knuckle-dragging predecessors without the need for chemical strait-jackets like Ritalin.[157]

While juicing is no substitute for eating the organic whole-foods themselves, it's a great way to pack nutrient-dense structures into the body free of pesticides, nitrates, preservatives and other junk. Juices taste great! One glass a day-perhaps two, but no more. Ideal if you are doing the no-breakfast, juice-before-noon routine (see **Free up Your Digestive Cycles**)

I heartily recommend Maria Costantino's excellent juicing 'bible', *The Handbook of Energy Drinks*.[158] In it, the author lays out dozens of easy-to-prepare juices that run the gamut from the fibrous righteous to the flat-out illegal. With the righteous ones, she catalogues the nutritional benefits and makes recommendations for particular ailments. Also covered are little snippets on each vegetable itself, along with a thumbnail sketch of their history. *Nice.*

In Summary: Juicing is an invaluable way to supplement your diet. Don't completely shy away from fruit juices, just be diligent in the amount you consume and when you consume them. Use veggies as your chief bulwark. *Give peas a chance!*

See also:
You Are What You Eat
Get in the Raw
Free up Your Digestive Cycles
Exercise Prevention

---

157 **Day, Phillip** *The Mind Game,* op. cit.
158 Available through www.credence.org

- 34 -
Own a Good Conscience

'Just two more laser treatments and the 'Roseanne' tattoo is gone from my chest.' - **Tom Arnold**

Forgive others.

Be forgiven.

Let there be no comeback.

A bad conscience is the best antidote to Valium there is. Unfortunately, preoccupations with guilt suppress more than just the desire to sleep; immune function is affected and with it all systems go into stress. You can worry yourself stiff, literally.

And I can easily say 'unburden yourself and move on', but a bad conscience imprisons and urges no action, so once again, forcing yourself to take mature action to resolve conscience will always move the game forward. If your efforts are heartfelt and genuine, others will appreciate it and the lifting of weight and a lighter step will be enjoyed as the outcome. Many issues revolve around family - the most painful usually do. Can these be resolved peacefully by *you* taking action to apologise or forgive? How much better will you feel when it's settled amicably? These are 'conscience blocks'. Nothing there upon closer inspection but the memory you froze in a moment.[159]

Be blameless.

---

159 **Buscaglia, Leo** *Love*, Slack Incorporated, 1972

~ 33 ~
Exercise Prevention
Don't get sick in the first place

Self-evidently, avoiding illness is far better than suffering it. Unfortunately, it's not your doctor's job to stop you getting sick, that's down to you. I aim to convince you you're worth saving, though the fact that you've made it this far in this book probably means you agree you're worth saving too!

We are fortunate to have well over a century's worth of excellent scientific observation in matters concerning longevity. In *Health Wars*, I cover the Hunzas, Abkhazians and other long-lived peoples and summarise the Principles of Longevity as follows:

1) Live in a toxin-free environment
2) Have an alkalised body system
3) Be well hydrated
4) Eat natural, properly constituted food
5) Be active
6) Maintain an optimism and positive outlook for the future

The main culprit in the Western world is the communal trough - heavy in acidic meats, sugars, milks, grains, trans-fats and chemicals, which boost levels of damaging fungi and yeast. A properly combined diet, rich in alkali-ash foods (unrefined, uncooked plant dietary) and low in proteins (20-40 g a day) is the way to go. The body takes in amino acids to build human proteins ideally from high quality vegetation, fruits and nuts, so you are not going to run short of protein any time soon. The watchwords are *balance* and *grazing*.

Bringing such common sense into your own existence is only a matter of forming the habit. And it's not as if real food doesn't taste great. Remember, I aim to convince you you're worth saving. If you agree a few simple changes each day could pay great dividends, you'll find the *Food For Thought Regimen* at the back of this book a great place to start. Avoiding disease involves deciding what you *don't* want and how badly you don't want it. Habits need to be changed and you have to want to change them. If you are already sick, *The ABC's of Disease* explains the research on a whole range of conditions and what you can do. Below are some great websites that can be searched with keywords on all manner of health subjects:

www.credence.org
www.mercola.com
www.doctoryourself.com
www.thedoctorwithin.com
www.newstarget.com

Books available from www.credence.org
Health Wars
Cancer: Why We're Still Dying to Know the Truth
The ABC's of Disease
The Little Book of Attitude
Food For Thought

- 32 -
Deal With Addictions

From annoying little speech tics to long-term substance abuse, addictions are a fact of life and millions of people live with them. Millions of people don't do something about them, though.

Malnutrition is at the heart of most, as well as repetitive behaviour in a state of emotion. On the nutrition front, a classically undernourished person with low blood sugar seeks a 'lift' to improve their mood. Food or substance abuse is the result. Repetitive behaviour carried out in a state of emotion will also establish an addiction as a comfort zone in the brain (Pavlov's Principle), especially if the activity concerned results in a perceived improvement of mood. *'Alcohol makes me forget...'* says the alcoholic, who might be grappling with emotional, financial or professional problems while seeking 'a release'.

Once the addiction sets in, there are biochemical and nutritional implications that need to be dealt with, along with the psychological factors. These are best treated side by side.

Symptoms of Addiction

Compulsive behaviour, insomnia, nightmares, violent mood swings, feelings of doom, hallucinations, craving for sweets and alcohol, fluctuating weight, hypo/hyperglycaemia, compulsive workaholic behaviour, extreme anxiety and nervousness.

Addiction and Hypoglycaemia

Alcoholics and drug addicts invariably have chaotic blood sugar. Dr Carl Pfeiffer reports that in 1973, when a group of 200 alcoholics was tested for glucose intolerance. 97% of them came up positive.[160] Those addicted to alcohol, drugs (recreational or pharmaceutical) and junk foods can manipulate their blood sugar and, hence, mood with their habits. This creates a dependence on these substances.

Addiction and Allergies

Often the addict can test positive for allergy with the substance to which they are addicted. Pfeiffer, Philpot and Kalita discovered over 75% of tobacco smokers showed a positive allergy for tobacco on skin tests.[161] Typically all addicts require a normalisation of blood sugar, a nutrient-dense, organic diet (the majority eaten raw to preserve amino acids and enzymes) and optimum supplementation.

Libby and Stone pioneered the use of mega-doses of intravenous Vitamin C in detoxifying heroin and methadone addicts. 30-85 grams a day were administered to 30 heroin addicts with 100% success.[162] Pawlek achieved significant results using 3 grams of Vitamin C and high doses of B3 niacin (up to 2 grams/day).[163] Alkali-forming diets are essential for the recovering alcoholic. In 1973, Blackman gave 19 heroin addicts sodium and potassium bicarbonate every half an hour for two hours, followed by a two-hour break, and repeated the cycle until withdrawal had been completed. The volunteers reported that

---

160 **Pfeiffer, Carl & Patrick Holford**, *Mental Illness - The Nutrition Connection*, ION Press, London: 1996

161 Ibid.

162 **Libby, AF & I Stone**, "The Hypoascorbemia-Kwashiorkor Approach to Drug Addiction Therapy: Pilot Study", *Orthomolecular Psychiatry*, 6(4),300-308:1977

163 Pfeiffer, Carl & Patrick Holford, op. cit. p.166

withdrawal symptoms were either completely or considerably reduced.[164]

The Fungi Conspiracy

A dependence on sweet things, including alcohol, will usually stir up a yeast infestation like *Candida albicans*. Symptoms are rashes around the genitalia (jock itch and vaginal yeast infections), toe-nail fungus, athlete's foot and four Mars Bars a day. A craving for sweets can often be the result of the yeast becoming hungry and increasing their discharge of mycotoxins, which suppress immune function and blood sugar. Sweets, alcohol and other foods inevitably follow ('the munchies'). These critters feature quite prominently in many conditions since they multiply and damage those who have abused themselves with modern 'convenience' foods and drinks.[165]

Breaking Patterns - The Carrot and the Stick

Addictions and habits also have another angle which must be dealt with, namely behavioural patterns. The brain uses patterning to establish behaviour it believes will assist it in surviving. Any behaviour repetitively carried out over a 15- to 30-day period in a state of positive emotion will be established as a pattern ('comfort zone'). Unfortunately bad patterns or addictions begin this way too. The key to patterning is understanding that the brain's most dominant human dynamic is survival, and the two key elements the brain uses to survive are:

- The need to avoid pain (the stick)
- The desire to gain pleasure (the carrot)

---

[164] Ibid.

[165] **Day, Phillip** *The ABC' of Disease,* Credence 2003. See also *Health Wars*

Breaking addictions necessitates the desire to *want to stop* (gaining leverage). Secondly, applying a consistent and effective approach that will get the results. In *The ABC's of Disease* under 'Addictions' I examine both the mental and physical aspects of substance and behaviour addiction and the strategies that can work to shut them down. In *The Mind Game*, I cover in much more detail today's fraudulent penchant for labelling lifestyle problems 'mental illnesses' and prescribing mind-altering drugs. If you think you have a problem in this area:

- Don't suffer unnecessarily
- Don't make others suffer unnecessarily
- Get educated
- If something about you needs changing, *you must change it*
- Seek professional guidance
- Decide to overcome
- *Never do nothing*

See also:
Set Goals Daily
Be an Overcomer
You Are What You Eat
Avoid Medical Testing Disease
Avoid Psychiatrists
Choose the Right Doctor

~ 31 ~
Avoid National Media

'Our job is not to give people what they want, but what we decide they ought to have.' - **Richard Salant, former president of CBS News**

In most countries there is a scurrilous, filthy, abominable media. For many it's hard to switch off. We are captivated by other people's problems, engaged by their tragedies, perhaps because our own lives have been made so infuriatingly dull we seem to crave this daily *frisson* of doom.

My opposition to media stems chiefly from the fact that a deliberate decision is made to screen only bad news (nocebos), almost all of which does not affect us directly. I wonder whether Mark Austin and Mary Nightingale really know the harm they are causing with their 30 minutes of death, mayhem and grief every evening. Followed, of course, by the usual soap opera engaged in the buzz-subjects of the moment: gay rights, arson, illegal immigration, and other matters peculiarly relevant to Yorkshire.

And I've come to the conclusion media steals our innocence and belief in the good of people, creates and destroys heroes, exists for no other reason than to inflame passions and create conflict. If media actually made the world a safer place by exposing wrongdoing (it's well-vaunted *raison d'être*), its worldwide début in the Twentieth Century - an era blighted with more wars, crime, drugs and sleaze than any other period in history - must make for dubious review.

As Josef Goebbels could have told you, propaganda makes such things possible. What kid in the sixties even *knew* what 'acid' was until Timothy Leary told him to tune in, turn on and drop out? Who could even find Saigon on a map? Without media, who would today's terrorism play to? Who's going to blow up a building or destroy an airliner if they are not able to gain the leverage of a world stage from which to put their case? Media fuels terrorism and I think the terrorists know this, which is why they seek to play to the world (Al Jazeera), and why the cameras are always whirring. Without such *free,* worldwide exposure for his agenda, martyrdom or a 'thirty stretch' don't seem like such a bargain to the anarchist.

'But the media exposes all kinds of atrocities!' people cry. Of course, and that's why we believe we need the media. Have you ever wondered why they don't tell us any good news? Only *News at Ten* used to do a little good news spot almost as an afterthought - Trevor McDonald smiling *'...and finally....'* and going on to tell about 'The Tamworth Two' - a couple of pigs who escaped from the slaughterhouse and were currently on the run from their executioners.

My point entirely.

These days on TV there are such bloody imaginings. Hostages paraded before a shaky handicam provoking the inevitable *'I'll not go to Europe, Elmer, they're not good to Americans there.'* Scaring a citizen into thinking ill of his neighbour. Terrifying the world with a whole arsenal of scenarios that never show up (bird flu, Hong Kong flu, SARS, aliens, Al Qaeda, HIV,[166] ricin in a North

---

[166] **Ransom, Steven and Phillip Day** *The Truth About HIV,* Credence, 2004

London bedsit). H L Mencken said it right. '*The whole aim of practical politics is to keep the populace alarmed, and hence clamorous to be led to safety, by menacing it with an endless series of hobgoblins, all of them imaginary.*'

Surprise, surprise, media skews our perceptions and wrote the seminal glossy on eating disorders, 'stars without slap', and the washed-up soap-goddess so forthright about her cocaine addiction. Media's become society's educator, which is not such good news since media sold out to Big Business decades ago, which these days pays big money to influence the torpid public mind.

Are you sick? Have a drug. A little depressed? Well, there's a drug. Too much Alan Sugar? Prozac or Ritalin. Eight million American kids a day can't be wrong. Then again, eight million American kids already think they're Bart Simpson.

Watching all that paedophilia, murder, Sex in the City and *I Have a Right to My Own Orgasm* on TV though, I've a mind to think it's all a far cry from the world *I* see every time I venture out of my front door. Blue-tits nibbling my nuts in the garden. Rona Seaforth on her way to the doctor's. Ken doing his window-cleaning round on his trailer-trike. No Osamas on my doorstep, just bin-liners. No car-bomb in Maidstone.

Tell me what force (other than psychiatry) has done more to distort and inflame society, and generate millions of anti-depressant prescriptions than the 30-minute, revolving 'news' atrocity? That Trojan Horse wheeled into my living room at it again, whinnying things that have nothing to do with me. And I'm paying for this Dantean illusion. To the Brussels Broadcasting Corporation, in fact.

Here We Go

Try four weeks without newspapers and TV, though God knows how you'll cope. What will you do with all the time? *Get a hobby. Meet people. Go places. Get a life.* And what if you do and your enjoyment returns, will you see media for what it really is? A priceless tool for proper education, hijacked by extremists who use it to impose minority agendas on a world still coming to terms with the size of Jordan André's breasts.

The Role of the Media

Many scoff at the notion the press can be appropriated and controlled, citing as obvious examples the various 'exposés' which rock our nations from time to time in the newspapers. Sceptics who disbelieve there exists a Media and Information Super Highway Old Boys' Club may wish to obtain the September 1998 edition of *Vanity Fair,* which contains Annie Liebovitz's remarkable photograph.[167]

Thirty-seven of the world's top mass communications purveyors gather in an Idaho wood for a photo-call? Their combined wealth totals $1.4 trillion. Their average age is 50 and between them they own 14 film studios, 43 music labels, 52 magazines and 124 daily newspapers. Cast your eyes down the following names and ask yourself a couple of questions:

- Are these busy people?
- What does it say about collective cooperation that they took valuable time off (some travelled halfway around the world)

[167] The photograph is also printed in the *Evening Standard,* 10th September 1998, pp.8-9

just to attend a photo shoot for *Vanity Fair* in *Idaho*, of all places?

Herbert A Allen, president, Allen and Company; **Edgar Bronfman Jr**, president, Seagram; **Howard Stringer**, president, Sony (US); **Gerald Levin**, chairman, Time Warner; **Richard Parsons**, president, Time Warner; **Michael Jordan**, chairman, CBS; **Jeffrey Katzenberg**, partner, Dreamworks SKG; **John Malone**, chairman, TCI; **Nathan Myrvold**, chief technology officer, Microsoft; **Michael Ovitz**, chairman, CKE Associates; **Jeff Berg**, chairman, ICM; **Warren Buffet**, chairman, Berkshire Hathaway; **Michael Armstrong**, chairman, AT&T; **Ted Waitt**, chairman, gateway; **Ron Meyer**, president, Universal; **Bob Pittman**, president, America Online; **James Kennedy**, chairman, Cox Enterprises; **Nobuyuki Idei**, president, Sony; **Sumner Redstone**, chairman, Viacom Inc; **Terry Semel**, chairman, Warner Bros; **Michael Bloomberg**, partner, Bloomberg; **Frank Biondi**, chairman, Universal; **Leo Hindrey Jr**, chairman, TCI; **Andrew Grove**, chairman, Intel; **Stephen Case**, chief executive, America Online; **Jonathan Dolgen**, chairman, Viacom Entertainments Group; **Katherine Graham**, proprietor, Washington Post; **Donald Graham**, chief executive, Washington Post; **Barry Diller**, chairman, USA Networks; **David Geffen**, partner, Dreamworks SKG; **Rupert Murdoch**, chairman, Newscorp; **Bob Wright**, president, NBC; **Herbert Siegel**, president, Chris-Craft; **Gordon Crawford**, senior vice president, Capital Research; **Peter Chernin**, president, Newscorp; **Brian Roberts**, president, Comcast; **Bill Gates**, chairman, Microsoft.

Head Illuminatus David Rockefeller was recorded saying the following words at the clandestine Bilderberger meeting in Baden Baden, Germany, in June 1991.

'We are grateful to the Washington Post, the New York Times, Time magazine and other great publications, whose directors have attended our meetings and respected their promise of discretion for almost forty years.... It would have been impossible for us to develop our plan for the world if we had been subject to the bright lights of publicity during those years. But today the world is more sophisticated and prepared to march towards a world government. The supranational sovereignty of an intellectual élite and world bankers is surely preferable to the national auto-determination practised in past centuries.' [168]

Intellectual Prostitutes

John Swinton, the former chief of staff of the *New York Times*, was called by his associates 'the dean of his profession'. As a luminary of international journalism and widely regarded as one of the most experienced newshounds of his day, Swinton was

---

[168] Liberty Lobby, *Bilderbergers: Spotlight on the Bilderbergers*, Deep River Books, Los Angeles, CA. The Bilderberg meetings were founded by HRH Prince Bernhard of the Netherlands, a former SS officer and employee of Nazi chemical empire, IG Farben. The group was named after the Bilderberg Hotel in Oosterbeck, Holland, where the first meeting took place in 1954. Comprising international financiers, politicians, media and other key global leaders, and by invitation only, the Bilderberg meetings are conducted in the strictest secrecy, at varying world venues, the agendas unpublicised, and the group's existence almost entirely unreported. All attempts by Credence to gain further information on the May 1998 Bilderberg meeting held at the Turnberry Hotel, Scotland, were met with *"No comment."* 1998 Turnberry attendees included Conrad Black, chairman UK *Telegraph Newspapers*, Anatole Kaletsky, associate editor UK *Times*, Christopher Hogg, chairman *Reuters*, Jim Hoagland, associate editor *Washington Post*, David Rockefeller, chairman of *Chase Manhattan Bank*, Henry Kissinger, *Kissinger Associates*, James Wolfensohn, president *World Bank*, Jan Leschly, CEO *SmithKline Beecham Pharmaceuticals*. For an insight into Bilderberg influence over the current British, European and US governments, visit www.watch.pair.com/discernment.html and related links.

asked to toast 'an independent press' at the New York Press Club. In so doing, some monumental statements about the servile and controlled condition of the media were made before an astounded, but perhaps not entirely disbelieving audience:

'There is no such thing at this date of the world's history, in America, as an independent press. You know it and I know it. There is not one of you who dares to write your honest opinions, and if you did, you would know beforehand that it would never appear in print. I am paid weekly for keeping my honest opinions out of the paper I am connected with. Others of you are paid similar salaries for similar things, and any of you who would be so foolish as to write honest opinions would be out on the streets looking for another job.

If I allowed my honest opinions to appear in one issue of my paper, before twenty-four hours my occupation would be gone. The business of the journalist is to destroy the truth; to lie outright; to pervert; to vilify; to fawn at the feet of mammon, and to sell his country and his race for his daily bread. You know it and I know it, and what folly is this toasting an independent press? We are the tools and vassals for rich men behind the scenes. We are the jumping jacks, they pull the strings and we dance. Our talents, our possibilities and our lives are all the property of other men. We are intellectual prostitutes.'[169]

---

169 **Kershaw, Peter** *Economic Solutions*, Quality Press, 2888 Bluff Street #315, Boulder, CO USA 80301

~ 30 ~
Be Brave! Have the Courage to Go On!

Facing up to your mountains is one of the hardest, most rewarding of the simple changes in this book. There's nothing enjoyable about confronting something that scares you. Mostly, if there's the odds-on chance you can avoid it, you will (the brain avoids pain).

We live in a 'peaceful' society, so war and pillage don't often visit my neighbourhood. The monsters instead will be social challenges; grief for a loved one, financial woes, an illness, a problem with work, yobs outside the pub. Symptoms of worry are a rapid heartbeat, blood pounding, counting sheep and getting past 1,000, fear of failing, fear of the unknown.

If you've been through the wringer, you've already learned a lot about yourself, and some of it you don't like, such as your real courage *vis à vis* the courage you show to others. Take heart. Being brave is not being without fear, it's being scared and having the courage to go on. As Winston once put it, 'Never, never, never, NEVER give up!' and who better than the old bulldog himself to know about dire straits, dark alleys and choosing the road less travelled by?

With Hitler's divisions poised across the Channel complete with a seemingly invincible Luftwaffe, and the shattered remnants of his own army recently disembarked from Dunkirk, a stark choice now confronted Churchill. Should he surrender to the damnable Nazis, or haul up the drawbridge and sentence Britain to what Poland got? History is replete with such moments of desperate endeavour and we know how they triumphed, and what happened when they didn't. Churchill's immortality derives largely from the fact that he was a *keen* war prime minister, and even with his back against the wall, the old boy famously chose to make Britain's darkest moment her finest hour:

'Even though large tracts of Europe and many old and famous States have fallen or may fall into the grip of the Gestapo and all the odious apparatus of Nazi rule, we shall not flag or fail. We shall go on to the end. We shall fight in France, we shall fight on the seas and oceans, we shall fight with growing confidence and strength in the air, we shall defend our Island, whatever the cost may be, we shall fight on the beaches, we shall fight on the landing grounds, we shall fight in the fields and in the streets, we shall fight in the hills; we shall never surrender.'

Words, turned into action.

We should train ourselves and our children in the skills required to overcome. Being brave is far easier when you take action. Taking action is predicated upon having a plan. Having a good conscience and leading a blameless life will also lend the moral courage to accept that bad things happen, and when they happen to us, we are better off getting through the best we can with the minimum of bitterness and bellyaching.

So be of good courage, these things too shall pass. Take action and help others do likewise, and like Britain and her Right Honourable Member for Cigars, this too could be your finest hour.

~ 29 ~
There is Danger in Excess, Moderation in All Things

The middle road again!

Is there any part of your life you are doing to excess? This is a warning sign. Working too late, worrying overly, staying up late, spending hours playing computer games, drinking too much.

Always strive for balance.

Most excesses have already generated behavioural patterns by the time you identify them as problems. **Deal With Addictions** will introduce you to tools which will help remove unwanted programming. I tend to get very compulsive with projects I am keen on, so I have to make a special effort to 'dilute' my enthusiasm or else I'm doing it 24/7. So I thin the action and savour the anticipation. Not all excesses are addictions, but most are.

See also:
Set Goals Daily
Take a Four-Week Holiday
Listen to What Comes Out of Your Mouth
Don't Lose Your Joy
Work at Self-Improvement
Deal With Addictions
Own a Good Conscience
Guard Input
Be Disciplined

- 28 -
Obtain Control Over Your Sense of Certainty

Know that you know why you do what you do

Obtain control over your sense of certainty when your problem is serious. Knowing why you're doing what you're doing helps you practise new habits and adopt them as 'lifestyle'. Millions take toxic medication without question because they don't *want* to know any better. It's easier to be told what to do, especially when you are frightened. Many with terminal debt do not possess the tools with which to tackle the problem, so they go to a loan shark to consolidate their borrowing and end up with a £400 payment for the next 300 years. Weight problems, lack of ambition, poverty, loneliness and depression are all areas in which we can personally intervene with spectacular results, in addition to any ministrations engaged in by our professionals.

Knowing you're on the right path has a terrific effect on immune function. Someone suffering from cancer, who embarks on a healthy regime, sends a powerful placebic message to their cells: *'All is well. Carry on, you little puff-balls.'*

Belief is the big enchilada, belief in what you are doing, why you're doing it, and an expectation that the utter right of your cause will produce the result. We know almost nothing about the mind-body connection other than it connects. The new science of psychoneuroimmunology is attempting to get to the bottom of it.[170] While we're waiting, we know enough to get started.

---

[170] www.pnirs.org

- Know why you're doing what you're doing
- Obtain control over your environment
- Develop values and stick to them
- Gain knowledge from more than one source
- Be wise in the ways of the world
- Believe in what you do even if others don't!

NEXT!

See also:
You're Never Too Old to Change
The Sky Rarely Falls In
Be an Overcomer
Think Good Thoughts, Don't Dwell on Evil
Work at Self-Improvement
Guard Input
Take Responsibility for Your Actions
Help Others

~ 27 ~
Live One Day at a Time

'The soil says, 'Don't bring me your need, bring me your seed.'' - **Jim Rohn**

Building value into each day may get a lot done, but when we live one day at a time *and enjoy what we do in the present,* it's hard not to enjoy with it the realisation we are really - well - *living.*

Most of us package our most precious resource. Those with 'boring' jobs know what I mean; exchanging time for money in a job no-one told us we had to save up for. In my youth, I did some of the guttiest, service-pistol-to-the-temple, most dragged-out, boring jobs on the planet, so I feel eminently qualified to comment as follows:

Interesting jobs are far better.

There's no easy way to say this, so I'll just say it. If you have a boring job and don't want to be bored, *change it.* Family and finances notwithstanding, trading time for money *and being bored while you do it* is the cruellest curse you can hex your life with.

- Don't live with regret
- Develop a cunning plan
- Go for the better day

Oh, some days I suffered! Soaked to the skin as a motorcycle messenger in my late teens in London, daily dodging death up Oxford Street, busting to pee like the skies were falling in, tearing off three layers of sodden protective clothing and jamming myself into elevators to make it to the fourth floor in time. These days, I'm definitely having better days.

- I plan every one of them (set goals)
- I give something to the day
- I take something from it
- I *expect* to be pleased with the results

If you don't live one day at a time, you'll have squandered your most precious resource by being somewhere else mentally for most of the week. More on this later. For now,

This is the day that has been appointed to you!

Live it!

See also:
Time is Your Most Precious Resource
Set Goals Daily
Think Good Thoughts, Don't Dwell on Evil
Live in the Present
Simplify, Simplify, Simplify
Never Retire
See the World and Have No Fear
Be Inspired
Guard Input
Help Others
Have a Point to it All

~ 26 ~
Climb Stairs Whenever You Can
Then climb 'em again!

Stair-climbing is shunned by most, yet a more remarkable form of aerobic exercise one can not imagine without all the dread of anticipating it.

'Oh, God, stairs!'
Climb them.
Then climb them again.

You can do it in the home. You can do it at the train station. Stair-climbing increases the heart-rate, works the lungs, and is a great, overall muscle-conditioner. I seem to live in hotels, so Samantha and I make a point of working the stairs at every opportunity. Stair-climbing machines are also great if you have a gym membership or the motivation to use one at home (I don't). When I lived in California, local residents would make use of a colossal flight of steps that ran up a Santa Monica hillside (200 steps at least). I went back there the other day. Dozens still show up from dawn onwards, young and old alike, and wheeze their way to the top. And then come down and do it all again.

Stair-climbing is one of the best exercises going, since its action is aerobic (oxygen-burning) and galvanises the metabolism. Don't overdo. Exercise to the degree that you're able, and consult a doctor if you have an existing condition.

'Counting steps instead of miles can boost your walking workout and save you time,' says www.prevention.com. *'Researchers in England and Northern Ireland asked 12 sedentary women to climb a 200-step staircase, progressing from once a day to six times a day (they were allowed to take the elevator down.) Each ascent took about 2 minutes, so by the end of the study, the women were exercising only 12 minutes a day.*

In less than 2 months, they saw a boost in their fitness level, along with improvements in their cholesterol level that were enough to cut their risk of cardiovascular disease by 33 percent.

'This is among the best evidence that short bouts of exercise can have tremendous health benefits," says study author Colin Boreham, PhD, of the University of Ulster in Northern Ireland.[171]

See also:
Set Goals Daily
Exercise - Walk 10,000 Steps a Day
Never Retire
Breathe Clean Air
Work at Self-Improvement
Exercise Prevention
Be Disciplined

---

[171] Maggie Spilner with Sarah Robertson, www.prevention.com

~ 25 ~
Avoid Repetitive Strain

Similar to **Pay Attention to Chronic Conditions**. The uniqueness of your daily ritual may be putting certain parts of your Highness under duress, resulting in creaky, arthritic limbs, heartburn, blood-sugar problems, depression, etc.

As we get older, our bad habits will definitely start telling on us. It's best to pick up these problems early, or the later you leave it, the harder the fix can become.

Think about any parts of you that tweak and aren't right. Carpal Tunnel Syndrome from all that typing? Eyesight strain? Backache? Heartburn from too many business lunches?

- Change your behaviour by changing your routine
- Little changes will do it
- Don't just take drugs and hope the pain will go away

See also:
Exercise Your Eyesight
Pay Attention to Chronic Conditions
There is Danger in Excess, Moderation in All Things

- 24 -
Avoid Sugar/Fat-Free Foods

While saccharin still remains controversial over whether or not it causes cancer, people turning to another sugar alternative have grown equally dismayed at the fur-fight over aspartame. You'll know it under the brand names Nutrasweet, Canderel, Equal, Spoonful and Equal-Measure, showing up in restaurants, coffee-shops and burger bars pretty much everywhere these days.

Aspartame was discovered by accident in 1965 by James Schlatter, a chemist working for G D Serle Company, who was testing anti-ulcer compounds for his employers. Aspartame's original approval as a sweetener for public consumption was blocked by neuroscientist Dr John W Olney and consumer attorney James Turner in August 1974 over concerns over both aspartame's safety and G D Serle's research practices. However, aspartame duly received its approval for dry goods in 1981 and its go-ahead as a sweetener for carbonated beverages was granted in 1983, despite worries over its neurological effects.[172] In 1985, G D Serle was purchased by pharmaceutical giant Monsanto, and Serle Pharmaceuticals and The NutraSweet Company were created as separate corporate identities.

---

[172] Two FDA scientists, Jacqueline Verrett and Adrian Gross, reviewed data from three studies which highlighted alleged irregularities in G D Serle's research procedures. The two government scientists declared that the irregularities they had uncovered were serious enough to warrant an immediate halt to aspartame's approval for use. *Food Magazine*, "Artificial Sweetener Suspicions", Vol. 1, No.9, April/June 1990.

According to researcher Alex Constantine in his essay entitled 'Sweet Poison', aspartame may account for up to 75% of the adverse food reactions reported to the US FDA, due primarily to its reported ability to affect neurological processes in humans. Dr Olney found that an excess of aspartate and glutamate, two chemicals used by the body as neurotransmitters to transmit information between brain neurons, could kill neurons by allowing too much calcium to collect in their cells to neutralise acid. This neurological damage led Olney to label aspartate and glutamate 'excitotoxins', in that they, according to Olney, 'excite' or stimulate the neural cells to death.[173]

Symptoms

Side-effects of aspartame poisoning have been variously reported as fits, convulsions, multiple sclerosis, Alzheimer's disease, ALS, memory loss, hormonal problems, hearing loss, epilepsy, Parkinson's disease, AIDS dementia, brain lesions and neuro-endocrine disorders. Risks to infants, children and pregnant women from aspartame were also underscored by the Federation of American Societies for Experimental Biology, a research body that traditionally follows FDA policy and adopts a 'softly-softly' approach to chemical problems. The Federation declared:

'It is prudent to avoid the use of dietary supplements of L-glutamic acid by pregnant women, infants and children. The existence of evidence for potential endocrine responses... would also suggest a neuroendocrine link and that... L-glutamic acid should be avoided by women of childbearing age and individuals with affective disorders.'[174]

---

173 *The Guardian*, London, UK, 20th July 1990

174 *Food Magazine*, "Artificial Sweetener Suspicions", op. cit.

Aspartame comprises two chief troublemakers:

Phenylalanine: The amino acid L-phenylalanine, used by the brain, comprises 50% of aspartame. People suffering from the genetic disorder phenylketonuria (PKU) cannot metabolise phenylalanine and so an excess of this amino acid builds up in parts of the brain, leading to a decrease of serotonin levels, bringing on emotional disorders and depression.

Methanol: Also known as wood alcohol. The poison methanol is a 10% ingredient of aspartame, which is created when aspartame is heated above 86°F (30°C) in, for example, the preparation of processed foods. Methanol oxidises in the body to produce formic acid and the neurotoxin, formaldehyde, also used in many vaccinations. Methanol is considered by America's Environmental Protection Agency (EPA) to be *'...a cumulative poison, due to the low rate of excretion once it is absorbed. In the body, methanol is oxidised to formaldehyde and formic acid; both of these metabolites are toxic.'*[175]

A one-litre carbonated beverage, sweetened with aspartame, contains around 56 mg of methanol. Heavy consumers of soft drinks sweetened with aspartame can ingest up to 250 mg of methanol daily, especially in the summer, amounting to 32 times the EPA warning limit. Which is not good news for humans, but quite good news for model aircraft.

Dr Woodrow C Monte, Director of the Food Science and Nutritional Laboratory at Arizona State University, was concerned that human response to methanol was probably much

---

175 *Extraordinary Science*, Vol. 7, No.1, Jan/Feb/Mar 1995, p.39

greater than with animals, due to humans lacking key enzymes that assist in methanol detoxification in other creatures. Monte stated: *'There are no human or mammalian studies to evaluate the possible mutagenic, teratogenic, or carcinogenic effects of chronic administration of methyl alcohol.'*[176]

Monte's concern about aspartame was so great he petitioned the FDA through the courts to address these issues. Monte requested that the FDA *'...slow down on this soft drink issue long enough to answer some of the important questions. It's not fair that you are leaving the full burden of proof on the few of us who are concerned and have such limited resources. You must remember that you are the American public's last defense. Once you allow usage* [of aspartame], *there is literally nothing I or my colleagues can do to reverse the course. Aspartame will then join saccharin, the sulfiting agents, and God knows how many other questionable compounds enjoined to insult the human constitution with government approval.'*[177]

Sadly, shortly after Dr Monte's impassioned plea, Arthur Hull Hayes, Jr, the Commissioner of the Food & Drug Administration, approved the use of aspartame in carbonated beverages. After that, he left the FDA to take up a position with G D Serle's public relations company![178] In 1993, the FDA further approved aspartame as a food ingredient in numerous process foods that would always be heated above 86°F as part of their preparation.

---

176 *The Guardian*, "Laboratory Animals Back from the Dead in Faulty Safety Tests", April/June 1990

177 Ibid.

178 Ibid.

Dr Joseph Mercola is no lover of aspartame. The well-known Internet doctor reports: *'In 1991, the National Institutes of Health listed 167 symptoms and reasons to avoid the use of aspartame, but today it is a multi-million dollar business that contributes to the degeneration of the human population, as well as the deliberate suppression of overall intelligence, short-term memory*[179] *and the added contribution as a carcinogenic environmental co-factor.*

The FDA and Centers for Disease Control continue to receive a stream of complaints from the population about aspartame. It is the only chemical warfare weapon available in mass quantities on the grocery shelf and promoted in the media. It has also been indicated that women with an intolerance for phenylalanine, one of the components of aspartame, may give birth to infants with as much as a 15% drop in intelligence level if they habitually consume products containing this dangerous substance.'[180]

People switching to sugar substitutes do so because they know sugar is bad but they still like the taste. Sugar addictions may indicate Candidiasis (Candida), chaotic blood sugar, insulin resistance (a precursor to diabetes) or other metabolic irregularity.[181] If you find yourself reaching for sugar-free products, *ask why.*

* * * * *

---

[179] The FDA instigated hearings in 1985 on aspartame at the request of Senator Metzenbaum, when a sample case was heard, in which a woman's memory suffered almost complete collapse until she ceased taking aspartame-laced products.

[180] Mercola, Joseph, www.mercola.com; Also **Steinman, D**, *Diet for a Poisoned Planet*, University of California study, p.190

[181] **Day, Phillip** *The ABC's of Disease,* op. cit.

Fat-Free? Fats Are Essential!

Which is why we call 'em *the essential fatty acids!* Junk fats are not. Guess which fats show up as the criminals in cholesterol reports?

The Technical Bit

Food processing has wrought havoc on daily intakes of genuine fats, generally referred to as the 'omegas'. It is estimated the population today may be consuming around one sixth of the omega-3's our ancestors ingested back in 1850, due mainly to today's food choices and processing.[182]

'Omega 3 fats are more susceptible to corruption during the cooking process,' states one technical report. *'EPA and DHA are omega-3 polyunsaturated fatty acids - the 'good fats'. Eicosapentaenoic acid (EPA) and docosahexaenoic acid (DHA) are in high concentrations in cold-water fish (e.g. salmon, tuna, mackerel and herring). EPA is used to support against high cholesterol and to form membranes surrounding cells.*[183] *EPA is required for the production of prostaglandins, which control blood clotting and other arterial functions.*[184] *DHA is a component of*

---

[182] Ibid.

[183] **Mizota, M, Katsuki, Y, Mizuguchi, K, Endo, S, Miyata, H, Kojima, M, Kanehiro, H, Okada, M, Takase, A, Ishiguro, J, et al.** "Pharmacological studies of eicosapentaenoic acid ethylester (EPA-E) on high cholesterol diet-fed rabbits", *Nippon Yakurigaku Zasshi* 1988 Apr;91(4):255-66

[184] **Bell, JG, Tocher, DR, MacDonald, FM, Sargent, JR**, "Diets rich in eicosapentaenoic acid and gamma-linolenic acid affect phospholipid fatty acid composition and production of prostaglandins E1, E2 and E3 in turbot (Scophythalmus maximus), a species deficient in delta 5 fatty acid desaturase", *Prostaglandins Leukot Essent. Fatty Acids* 1995 Oct;53(4):279-86

human brain and the retinal tissue.[185] [186] *DHA serves in the transmission of nerve impulses in the nervous system.'*[187]

Omega 3 Deficiency Symptoms: Dry skin, lack of co-ordination or impaired vision, inflammatory health problems, allergic reactions, memory or learning ability impaired, tingling in the arms or legs, hard to lose weight, high blood pressure or triglycerides, prone to infections.[188]

An imbalanced consumption of Omega-6 to -3 fats, mostly brought on through the western diet, leads to a whole host of problems. A Purdue University study indicated children low in Omega-3 fatty acids were significantly more likely to be hyperactive, have learning disorders, and display behavioural abnormalities.[189] A healthy diet, including oily fish and some sensible supplementation, will help prevent such woes. Dr Joseph Mercola states:

'Over 2,000 scientific studies have demonstrated the wide range of problems associated with Omega-3 deficiencies. The American diet is almost devoid of Omega 3's, except for certain types of fish. In fact, researchers believe that about 60% of Americans are deficient in Omega-3 fatty acids, and about 20%

---

[185] **Ward, GR, Huang, YS, Xing, HC, Bobik, E, Wauben, I, Auestad, N, Montalto, M, Wainwright, PE**, "Effects of gamma-linolenic acid and docosahexaenoic acid in formulae on brain fatty acid composition in artificially reared rats", *Lipids* 1999 Oct;34(10):1057-63

[186] **Neuringer, M**, "Infant vision and retinal function in studies of dietary long-chain polyunsaturated fatty acids; methods, results, and implications", *Am. J. Clin. Nutr.* 2000 Jan;71(1Suppl):256S-67S

[187] Neways briefing document. www.neways.com

[188] Day, Phillip, *The ABC's of Disease,* op. cit. A Guide to Nutritional Supplements

[189] Curr Atheroscler Rep. 2001 Mar;3(2):174-9

have so little that test methods cannot even detect any in their blood.

The human brain is more than 60% structural fat, just as your muscles are made of protein and your bones are made of calcium. But it's not just any fat that our brains are made of. It has to be certain types of fats, and we no longer eat these types of fats like we used to.

Worse, we eat man-made trans-fats and excessive amounts of saturated fats and vegetable oils high in Omega-6 fatty acids, all of which interfere which our body's attempt to utilize the tiny amount of Omega-3 fats that it gets.

Other parts of our bodies also need Omega-3 fatty acids. Symptoms of fatty acid deficiency include a variety of skin problems such as eczema, thick patches of skin, and cracked heels.' [190]

See also:
You Are What You Eat
Get in the Raw
Take a Basic Supplement Program (including fish oils!)

---

190 www.mercola.com/2001/sep/8/omega_3.htm

- 23 -
Don't Break the Law

'If this is the way Queen Victoria treats her prisoners, she doesn't deserve to have any.' - **Oscar Wilde**

Most have broken the law at one time or another. In fact, these days in the EU, I'm probably breaking 36 of them just sitting here typing you this! The fact is, the law is sometimes an ass, but it's the law. And actually, a constitutional democracy is all about possessing the apparatus to change or do away with unjust laws as new parliaments see fit. At least, that's the theory.

I chose this one because there are two issues connected with it that are bothering some who write in. Firstly, our attitudes towards the law, and secondly, our own loss of self-esteem whenever we break it.

These days, as you know, my attitude towards British justice has hardened. The criminal is frou-froued while the victim is frotted. The Human Rights Act has unleashed the dreaded compensation culture and every 'victim' and his dog are currently availing themselves of the taxpayer's pie. Worse, the apparatus to unseat unjust laws has been summarily disconnected, since all laws now originate in Brussels, and good luck finding anyone there you can vent your spleen on, if it will do any good, which it won't.[191]

People respect a country with just laws. Those who break the law feel more aggrieved at their separation from such a society. The balance is a fine one between Gestapo-like overlording and no

---

[191] **Day, Phillip** *Ten Minutes to Midnight*, Credence, 2004

law at all. A citizen deserves to feel safe in the knowledge the police will protect them in a consistent, understandable way. Today in Britain, where police won't even turn up unless you're in fifteen pieces and Kosovan, there's a curious juxtapositioning of the lawless with the pastoral. Most living in the villages around me don't break the law, but now live in fear of the other lot who do.

- Don't break the law. It's the law
- You think less of yourself for being on the wrong side of it, despite what you think
- Don't behave like a victim even if you are one
- Support organisations dedicated to the overthrowing of unjust laws
- Join your local Neighbourhood Watch group
- Be blameless
- If you are dissatisfied, demand a proper service from the police, *whom you pay*
- Aside from social reasons, consistent bad behaviour can be caused by bad diet
- **Attack Political Correctness** wherever you find it
- Steer the middle course and be zealous for good
- **Help Others**

See also:
Admit When You're Wrong
Listen to What Comes Out of Your Mouth
Attack Political Correctness
Manage Your Anger
Own a Good Conscience
Start Complaining
Take Responsibility for Your Actions

- 22 -
Fast Every Now and Then for Five Days

Once or twice a year, take the strain off the digestive system by fasting for five days on water and diluted fruit/veggie juices. The effects are stupendous and a lot of old gut-rubbish gets flushed out - a far more satisfactory way to feel cleaner, fresher and more vigorous than visiting the carwash with the windows wound down.

See also:
Free Up Your Digestive Cycles
Do a Bowel Cleanse
Juice Veggies
You Are What You Eat
Get in the Raw

- 21 -

Finding the Right Person is Being the Right Person

'Remember, blood is not only thicker than water, it's much more difficult to get off the carpet.' - **Phyllis Diller**

Looks aside, if you're going to sleep with the same person for the next fifty years, you probably need to know something about them.

Many relationship problems stem from an imbalance in the values department.[192] You don't believe in the things your partner believes in, you're not motivated the same way. The behavioural experts all agree incompatible values produce highly fractious relationships - years of university, that.

No-one likes to talk about values since politics and religion enter the picture. Then again, if you are heir to Lord Hobnob and you're about to marry Ken Livingstone's daughter, a values match of some kind could swing the odds of survival in your favour. And avoid your manor carp ending up in the London Aquarium at £10 a peek.

- Values make up your personality
- Values determine your character
- Your values attract or repel others
- Values, like goals, can give you direction
- They're what you believe in
- And tell others what they're getting themselves into

---

[192] www.anthonyrobbins.com

See also:

You're Never Too Old to Change
Set Goal Daily
Be an Overcomer
Admit When You're Wrong
Listen to What Comes Out of Your Mouth
Don't Lose Your Joy
Work at Self-Improvement
Manage Your Anger
Own a Good Conscience
Obtain Control Over Your Sense of Certainty
Don't Break the Law
Dare to Dream
Be Inspired
Avoid Dreamkillers
Experience Success
Be Thankful
Help Others
Have a Point to it All

- 20 -
Dare to Dream

'What makes Clint Eastwood, a middle-aged actor who has played with a chimp, think he could have a future in politics?' - **Ronald Reagan**

Everybody should have a dream. What's yours?

In the past when the going got tough, I dreamt an idyllic existence of being an author, writing books to help people, travelling the world, and looking out of my study window at a rose garden while I courted the Muse with my laptop. *Well, guess what?*

The scale of the dream does not matter but you have to want it. Organising a village fête or boot sale; getting married; rowing up the Amazon. Hitler polished off a whole box of chocolates and then invaded Russia (wish he'd stuck to the painting). There are dreamers who only dream, then there are the Dreamweavers who dominate their dream, refine, interrogate, nurture and nourish it, shepherd it onward to its restless, uncontainable fulfilment.

Take care what you dream for, you may get it.

Dreamweavers cannot help but try to turn their dreams into reality. Writers cannot help writing. Artists cannot help creating. Nurses cannot help serving. Politicians cannot help blowing hot air. We're too busy, so there's no depression if the dream inspires us. We have a goal - our engine, that thing that drives us - our passion, motivation, the drop-down, drag-out desire to move from where we are now to where we want to be in the future.

- Do you have a dream you have a chance of fulfilling?
- What's stopping you?
- Is that really the reason?
- Are you frightened of failing?
- *Are you inspired?*

A Reminder

As already covered, what everyone ultimately strives for is a state. An emotion. Desiring physical possessions is all very well, but it's what these possessions do for us that's the salient factor. Dreams are states wherein the outcome can already be observed, if not partially experienced.

- What state are you yearning for?
- Peace? Excitement? Stability? *Pride? Revenge? Frustration?*
- Are you materially driven?
- What do you expect your dreams to do for you?

Understanding the state you're striving for is the lynch-pin. Dreams are goals. In daring a dream, you are selling yourself on a course of action, a future wherein the dream is reality and the state fully potentised. Is the state you are seeking a noble one, or will it be produce nocebic emotions such as anger, hate and frustration?

It's worth doing the following exercise to find out what your dreams are and what states you expect from them.

- I dream of a louder exhaust on my car than all the other kids on the block. *Pride. Revenge.*
- I dream of marrying Jennifer Connelly. *Pride - It's what JC can do for you. You don't even know her*

- I dream of becoming rich. *Pride. Sloth. Revenge. Stability. Peace*
- I dream of winning the London Marathon. *Achievement. Pride. Excitement. Contentment*
- I dream of visiting Egypt. *Excitement. Wonder. Happiness. Fulfilment*
- I dream of having three kids, a whippet, an Aston Martin, Eminem rapping at my wedding, a hot-tub in the back yard, yadda, yadda, yadda -

    - See? Dreams sell states you might want to invest in
    - The state the dream fulfils is what you're really looking for
    - Wholesome states are more fulfilling than torrid ones
    - Set aside time each day to cast your mind to roamin'
    - Ask yourself: *What do I really want?*
    - Then ask yourself: *Why do I want it?*

Only You -

...know what motivates you. As a dreamweaver you can add purpose and context to your life. No goals equals no context to your existence, which can provoke the helpless, 'What's the point of it all?' Dreamweavers never fall victim. You dared the dream. The dream gives you pleasure. The project is responsible and worthy. It sparked you up in the first place, remember?

What Have I Learned?

- I must not fear to dream, it is only dreaming
- Dreams I enjoy bring me pleasure
- I will dwell on the dreams I am passionate about
- I can choose what I want out of life from my desires (the scale does not matter)

- What talents do I have which I *really* enjoy using?
- What *really* motivates me?
- Am I restless to achieve what motivates me?
- Will my desires and goals bring meaning to my life?

See also:
You're Never Too Old to Change
Set Goal Daily
Be an Overcomer
Work at Self-Improvement
Be Inspired
Avoid Dreamkillers
Experience Success
Be Thankful
Help Others
Have a Point to it All

~ 19 ~
Be Inspired

'We've got to pause and ask ourselves, how much clean air do we need?' - **Chrysler chairman, Lee Iacocca**

Making a conscious decision about where you are going is a fundamental necessity for all journeys, even if your desire is to drift where life takes you. Depression is an inability to take action. Often no goals are set, leaving us wandering aimlessly, wondering at the point of it all.

So you want to go to university. To study what? What do you want to achieve with your anthropology degree? You want to be a professional footballer? Write it down. You want to open your own hairdressing salon? How badly? Go to next year's concert at Glastonbury? Write a book? Gape at the pyramids of Giza or the Grand Canyon? Get busy scratching pen to paper. Are you inspired? *You have no idea?!!*

Inspiration's a state, it's what moves you. When I hear from someone who is depressed/suicidal/listless/apathetic, it's often their motor that needs firing up. There's no action. They feel barnacle-encrusted, forgotten and useless, that there's nothing left for them here. Back to the bookstore for you, chief.

Alternatively, thrust yourself into some physical action. Any action. Embark on an experience which is unfamiliar but enjoyable. Learn a new skill, a boat-trip down the Nile, play paintball, a swim in the sea, a London show, ride a horse through the rainforest - all will anchor you in the present and *force* you to respond to what's happening *now*, even if you squeal 'I'm a Celebrity - Get Me Out of

Here!' Getting a smile to thy gnarled features means you're making progress.

Once, during an unbelievably intense exam year at Charterhouse, I got very depressed. I didn't know what I wanted, all the revising going on in my head, and for what? I had no clue what I wanted out of life. Then one weekend a friend took me for a hair-raising ride on his Triumph Bonneville and by the time I returned for a rollicking from my housemaster, this lad was cured. I'd never been on a motorbike before and I can tell you - fifteen, male and rebellious? - the experience made quite an impression.

For the next seven years I went motorbike mad. To own one I had to get a job. To get a job I had to pass my exams. In fact, I passed my exams with flying colours, then set up my own motorcycle messenger company so I could ride 'em round the clock *and* get paid for the pleasure! I ran diamonds to Vienna, strange hoe-like implements to Holland. Most of the work, though, was around England's south-east, and I came to know London better than any black cab-driver, since they didn't have to know the suburbs like we did, and besides, black cabs were the enemy.

After a few years, I got bored with getting rained on, so I sold the business and left with some pals to Los Angeles, and we set one up there. All our thugs rode around tanning themselves all day long on sawn-off Kawasakis, wearing their sexy lightning-bolt tabards, working for LA's finest, lawyers, medicos, the film studios - even a few of the stars. I delivered to Dustin Hoffman, Steve Martin and Bob Newhart - all cool. Cybil Shepherd made me tea. Brian Dennehy gave me a tip. Madonna told one of us to @&** off in Bel Air (she thought we were paparazzi, this was before she got the muscles). Ah, the margaritas and surf - I'll never forget it. We were young, we were wild, we were well over the speed limit. And all that fun from an irresponsible bike-ride through Godalming?

Be safe!

Be inspired!

~ 18 ~
Avoid Dreamkillers

'Jeff Koon's work is the last bit of methane left in the intestines of the dead cow of post-modernism.' – **Robert Hughes**

Dreamkillers project their own doubts and failures onto others, and all dreamweavers have a school of them cluttering their wake, taking nibbles like *remorae* on a big fish.

The worst dreamkillers are often well-intentioned family members or friends who don't want you to fail. When the dreams become reality, the dreamkillers then discuss how soon your project will crash and burn, as it may have once done with them, which is why they have failed ever since to muster the courage to dream further. It's done out of love, but take my advice, avoid dreamkillers.

- There's probably one within ten yards of where you are sitting right now
- Take advice on new projects from impartial, professional acquaintances (v. important), not only from family and friends, who'll toss the idea under the bus at the first opportunity
- Be prudent with inspiration. Don't flog a dead horse. Differentiate between the light at the end of the tunnel and the train coming the other way
- Don't *you* be a dreamkiller!

See also:
The Sky Rarely Falls In
Admit When You're Wrong
Don't Gamble

- 17 -
Experience Success

Experience is what you get when you didn't get what you wanted

- Define at what point you will succeed at a task
- Success is accomplishment, the outcome of goal-setting
- Success is sweet only because there's failure
- Successful people know all about failure but learn from their mistakes
- Success and failure develop life skills
- Celebrating is an all-important part of the success ritual
- You conquered this challenge
- You will conquer the next challenge
- And show others how they can conquer too

Or, if you're a student, you can cheat and contact Barclay Littlewood's web-site and his lot will write your essays and first-class dissertations for you. Yes, really:

'The entrepreneur at the centre of the cash-for-essays controversy revealed... the biggest demand comes from the élite students of Cambridge University. Barclay Littlewood, whose company ukessays.com rakes in up to £90,000 a week by charging for essays written to order, made the astonishing claim as MPs and academics expressed outrage at the scale of online plagiarism. Mr Littlewood, 28, says the business he set up just three years ago now turns over £1.6 million a year. His team of 3,500

specialist writers have churned out more than 15,000 essays for lazy or time-pressed students.'[193]

Oh dear.

See also:

Be an Overcomer
Think Good Thoughts, Don't Dwell on Evil
Strive For Excellence
Laugh a Lot
Don't Gamble
Be in Love
Work at Self-Improvement
There is Danger in Excess, Moderation in All Things
Live One Day at a Time
Dare to Dream
Be Inspired
Avoid Dreamkillers
Be Disciplined
Be Thankful
Have a Point to it All

---

193 Mail on unday, 30th July 2006, p.38

~ 16 ~
Guard Input

Confucius say, 'Eagles may soar, but weasels don't get sucked into jet engines.'

It's a jungle out there.

What we focus on becomes our reality.

What's going on in Equador?

Who cares? I'm not focused on Equador.

What am I focused on?

And what is it doing to me?

'One study involving more than 700 families found that 14-year-old boys who watched relatively more television were more likely to have assaulted or committed a serious act of aggression against someone by the time they were 22 years old. A similar pattern was found among females, but the relationship was much weaker. Another study found that violence in the media can have a profound effect on the behaviour of children and teens and that TV violence is associated with aggression among children as young as 4 years.

Preschoolers who watch television violence and play violent video games are more likely to show high levels of aggression and antisocial behaviour than those not exposed, according to another study.' [194]

Input

... is everything we allow to enter us.
What we consume
What we see
What we hear
What we experience
What we touch
What we smell

Output

...is our reaction to the above:
Our deeds
Thoughts
Patterning
Emotions

The more positive the input (placebo), the more positive the output. The more positive the patterns, the more positive the performance. The reverse is true for nocebos.

If you suffer from lack of motivation, depression, listlessness, suicidal thoughts, etc - ***GUARD INPUT.*** Media, for instance, is input and changes the way we interpret the world, chooses what we see. Constant repetitions override and re-write opinions and patterning. Media is neuro-associative conditioning on steroids. It can be a force for good. Then again, through selective reporting, all Roman Catholic priests can become paedophiles, all dark-

---

[194] www.mercola.com

featured, moustachioed Middle-Easterners can become terrorists, and all felons in the Los Angeles County area will be 5' 10", 160 lb black males in their early twenties with no shirt on. You get the picture.

Televised imagery affects real-world behaviour in every way - the ad industry depends on it. The brain, on a sub-conscious level, cannot distinguish between what it experiences and what it is shown. Bad news brings us pain. Good news brings pleasure. The Six O'Clock News is almost all bad news, which means The Six O'Clock News = pain/nocebo. Most of what is covered is none of your business and does not affect you directly, yet you subconsciously take on the pain *and pay for it!* (*see* **Avoid National Media**)

Remember, environment plays a crucial role in patterning. If you are trying to change your own or someone else's behaviour, a change of environment often works wonders (*see* **Be Inspired** and **Take a Four-Week Holiday**).

- 15 -
Enjoy Silence

One of the most effective ways to guard input is to turn off the radio, switch off the TV, unplug the stereo, put the Ipod in the fridge, turn all clanking, buzzing, humming and grinding contraptions *orf* and enjoy peace.

Stop what you are doing now and listen. The chances are there's something going on in the background. Noise like light is ubiquitous these days and peace is no longer the prerogative of the country-dweller. Samantha and I often go for a walk in Bedgebury Forest and there's always an airliner overhead. One afternoon, we actually waited to see how long it would take for everything to revert to nature. We got fed up waiting, and if we did, I'm pretty sure the squirrels do too.

Mother Teresa of Calcutta said, *'See how nature - trees, flowers, grass - grows in silence; see the stars, the moon and the sun, how they move in silence... we need silence to be able to touch souls.'*

It goes without saying the hard-heads of the business world stumbled upon this technique long ago (not least to silence dissent). Top-7-Business, a personal development web-site catering for the business professional, lists its 'seven powers of silence' as follows:

- Silence is creative
- Silence builds trust
- Silence gives rest

- Silence brings balance
- Silence promotes the inner
- Silence promotes the real
- Silence allows listening.[195]

Another site is not so sure. *'Silence can be a frightening thing. There are times when silence is unnerving, humiliating or just plain boring. If you are speaking in front of a crowd and you lose your train of thought, the silence is torture. If you're in the midst of a crowd of strangers and there is no one you can talk to, the silence can be very lonely. The silence of walking down a dark alleyway late at night can be petrifying.*

'In addition, not everyone feels comfortable in his or her own skin. The idea of spending quiet time alone is anathema to such people. They fill their days with friends, family and co-workers. They do everything possible to avoid being by themselves. Eating a meal alone is an agonizing concept. Spending a whole evening with nothing but their own thoughts is even worse - give them a television and a remote control, at least!'[196]

In fairness, AllSpiritFitness goes on to make the all-important point:

'It's not really silence itself that gets to us, rather, it's our inner chatter that keeps us from appreciating quiet time. The mind has been a busy and active instrument for eons. Meditation would never have been invented if there hadn't been a need to train the mind to be still. But these days, between the Internet, television and full schedules, our thoughts are more than mere

---

[195] www.top7business.com

[196] http://www.allspiritfitness.com/library/features/aa063003a.shtml

whirlwinds - they're tempests. Even those of us who yearn for some quiet time alone are hard pressed to locate a few free minutes. We need to make sure that any silent time we get is also quality time.'[197]

- Inner chatter = patterning
- Silence calms the heart rate
- Silence lowers blood pressure
- Forget the radio, try driving around with nothing on
- Dwell for five minutes in silence and see how extraordinary the experience is
- What your mind throws up in the tranquil moments may also indicate areas of your life that might need addressing

Simple Changes concepts are designed to rid the mind of unwanted 'inner chatter'. The first place to start is reorganising your space so that noise is kept to a minimum. TV and radios switched off, washers and driers relocated to the garage/outhouse, Heathrow told to change its approach routes. Consider how useful silence could be for the following, if you learned how to change the quality of the mind's 'inner chatter' and thus your focus:

The Sky Rarely Falls In, Be an Overcomer, Put Plants Around the Place, Think Good Thoughts, Don't Dwell on Evil, Live in the Present, Admit When You're Wrong.

Simplify, Simplify, Simplify, Reconcile Your Fear of Death. Breathe Clean Air. Strive For Excellence. See the World and Have No Fear, Master Yourself.

---

[197] Ibid.

Turn Off the TV, Don't Lose Your Joy, Be in Love, Sleep in Pitch Darkness/Get Enough Sleep, Work at Self-Improvement, Create Overwhelming Optimistic Experiences, Manage Your Anger, Reward Yourself.

Give Yourself Permission to Recover, Own a Good Conscience, Deal With Addictions, Be Brave - Have the Courage to Go On, Obtain Control Over Your Sense of Certainty, Live One Day at a Time.

Finding the Right Person is Being the Right Person, Dare to Dream, Be Inspired, Experience Success, Take Responsibility For Your Actions, Be Disciplined, Read a Good Book, Be Thankful, Have a Point to it All.

~ 14 ~
Start Complaining

'Who is General Failure, and why is he reading my hard disk?' - **Steve Wright**

Inappropriately straight after silence is the need to complain when something isn't right. A few decades ago, *they'd* never have got away with it. Today, with good service and fairmindedness out of the window, *they* make an art out of getting away with it.

- Not all outrage is negative
- You have indignation, annoyance, offence, high dudgeon, huff, gall, pique, rankling and Basil Fawlty
- The great (and infamous) names of history were all agitators, so you've got company
- Anger without action is impotence (unhealthy)
- Righteous anger *with* action, while possibly earning you four-to-five in minimum security at HM's pleasure with a cell-mate by the name of Bubba, might also get you a 187-foot statue erected in your honour in Trafalgar Square with pigeons doing their business on top of your hat
- Depends what you mean about *righteous*

For twenty years I've campaigned against the medical system, corrupt politicians, bad justice, the EU, and stickers in the backs of cars saying *Pull Back, Give My Child a Chance* (like I wouldn't if they weren't). The lawful approach, I find, is best, not least to avoid speaking to your mother through reinforced glass using a phone screwed to the wall so you won't nick it.

The world is not a perfect place but there are bits of it I'd like to change. The Campaign for Truth in Medicine was founded to educate the public on public-domain information they weren't being told about - information that has, quite literally, saved lives. In addition, I complain about bad service. I steam at injustice. I don't like the 'Strawberry Surprise' to be because I can't have any. I don't appreciate the extractor fan in my hotel bathroom sounding like a bloody Luftwaffe raid over Croydon. Do I smoulder in silence? Not this suffering servant.

I am a veteran complainer. A whingeing Pom. The Ayatollah of Outrage. A stern stirrer of passions. I care about the world enough to want to help it, so my motives are pure. I'm wise with my time. If I'm piqued enough to lumber up on my high horse about something, then I want it changed and right now would do better than sometime next week.

- If I'm not happy, I do something about it (take action)
- I try to be fair
- Legal
- Moral
- Explain why I'm upset
- I can't and won't try to change everything - they'll be nothing left for Ben Elton to be wrong about
- Sudden anger is something else (*See* **Manage Your Anger**)
- When I've finished complaining, I revert to the previous chapter and enjoy silence
- After that, I start complaining again

See also:
Attack Political Correctness
There is Danger in Excess, Moderation in All Things

Manage Your Anger
Don't Lose Your Joy
Be an Overcomer
Think Good Thoughts, Don't Dwell on Evil
Strive For Excellence
Have a Point to it All

~ 13 ~

Don't be Dysfunctional Around Money

'Today's payslip has more deductions than a Sherlock Holmes story.' - **Raymond Cvikota**

Some people are plain funny around money. Here's what I've learned:

- **Get Out of Debt**
- Don't lend money to a friend, it's the quickest way to lose both
- Pay workmen on time
- Return money you've borrowed promptly and don't borrow again
- If you do a job for a friend and they insist on paying you, *a workman is worthy of his wages* (Matthew 10:10). They don't mind giving it, and you don't mind taking it
- Identify dysfunctionally repetitive behaviour around money and take action: Abuse of credit cards, stealing, Tightwad Syndrome, poverty mentality, withholding money as a weapon, living beyond your Two Jags and other unsavoury practices
- Healthy finances come from healthy goals
- Your goals are to increase income, reduce expenditure, live within your means and overcome bad habits
- Money is not a state but the *cause* of many
- Money is a tool, not an altar

See also:

Get Out of Debt
Deal With Addictions
Be Thankful
Help Others

~ 12 ~
Be Polite (But Don't Be Walked Over)

'I like to travel in non-British ships. None of that nonsense about women and children first.' – **Somerset Maugham**

Society has changed incredibly over the past fifty years and I'm not against all of it. There's no question we've benefited – people live longer, have wider food choices and don't die of the scourges we once used to. Then again, we do suffer from diseases today that would have boggled our forebears: Chronic Tax Anxiety Syndrome, Lottery Stress Disorder, Tourettes, the desire to tell someone to Foxtrot Oscar as a matter of first, rather than last resort.

I've been boring you with my disgust for the 'new morality', wherein integrity, innocence, respectability and truth have become casualties of the belief that everything in society needed changing when it didn't. Politeness has gone into the dustbin too, which I happen to think is a bad thing, and I hope you do too.

Being polite is the ability to listen, to extend to others their right to a viewpoint. It's been a casualty to minority opinion because politeness doesn't like what it sees but it's too polite to get in your face about it. Manners maketh the man or woman. Politeness says something about you in your interaction with the world. It's right there in the thesaurus next to Courtesy, Refinement, Culture and Civility. And that, as my old French teacher used to say, is the bastard of it.

On 1st May 1997, Tony Blair and the British Labour Party were elected to power with a crushing majority. The extraordinary thing, however, was not the totality of Mr Blair's victory, unparalleled in recent times, but rather the symbolism the election itself came to represent. The Old Order that trudged despairingly to the polls that May day was the dying Christian Britain of Kenneth More and Sir John Mills, of *Land of Hope and Glory* and *The Last Night at the Proms;* the sort of Britain reflected in the *Cruel Sea, The Dambusters* and other films still playing on a rainy Sunday afternoon. In contrast, the New Britain that powered to victory that spring day was mostly state-educated and -employed, atheist or agnostic, hip, trendy and gay, many of whom were deeply offended by the patriotism, duty and deference encouraged by the Old Order.

The writing had long been on the wall. George Orwell was constrained to write in *The Lion and the Unicorn* back in 1941,

'In intention, at any rate, the English intelligentsia are Europeanised. They take their cookery from Paris and their opinions from Moscow. In the general patriotism of the country they form a sort of island of dissident thought. England is perhaps the only great country whose intellectuals are ashamed of their own nationality. In left-wing circles it is always felt that there is something slightly disgraceful in being an Englishman and that it is a duty to snigger at every English institution, from horse racing to suet puddings. It is a strange fact, but unquestionably true, that almost any English intellectual would feel more ashamed of standing to attention during 'God Save the King' than of stealing from a poor box.'

By the time peace broke out, Britain was in the thrall of a deep moral and spiritual fatigue not even victory could extirpate. The Empire was broken, the Old Order dying, content to find a quiet corner to wheeze into to gather some peace before passing. Ironically, a nation grown weary of attack, slaughter and misery on such a Herculean scale now faced its greatest threat in the deceptive anti-climax of the post-war years. More deadly than a flotilla of Scharnhorsts, more insulting than the crash of ten thousand jackboots up Whitehall, the liberal-socialist revolution unleashed its ambush on the Old Order from a direction the latter could never have expected.

The counter-culture of the 1960's shocked, not only because of its anti-authoritarian signature, but also in the way it successfully hijacked the media and changed our behaviour. Many of the liberal intelligentsia of which Orwell wrote were burrowed deep in the arts and were well-positioned to carry out such a *coup*. Though TV was still a recent enough *imprimatur* of the Old Way to carry clout, BBC accents began changing, the war-weary Brit soon found himself chuckling at the outrageous, lampooned images he saw of himself on TV. Religion, morality and patriotism took a complete beating and were blamed for the war. The newly-birthed pop culture wrote countless songs damning the Old Guard as warmongering, sexually repressed and a danger to everyone. Targets previously considered sacrosanct became juicy targets. *The Life of Brian* lampooned Jesus. *This Was the Week that Was* mocked those who had lost their lives over Germany. New TV personalities like Jonathan Miller, Peter Cook, John Cleese and Alan Bennett were astonishingly different from anything the public had ever seen before - far cleverer, more amusing and incisive than those watching them could ever be.

The transforming effect on society's behaviour was total. Too young to remember the rationing of bacon to one ounce, Baby-Boomers found themselves increasingly isolated from, and suspicious of their parents. They couldn't understand the quaint moral reserve and sense of duty. Were insulted by the disapproval of the social and sexual freedom espoused by the New Age.

'As the war generation grew old,' Peter Hitchens writes, '*they found themselves living on an alien landscape where their traditional morals and values were increasingly mocked and derided by each generation which followed.... The society they now lived in, where the word of television was law, suddenly allowed only one point of view to be expressed openly, and it was not theirs....*'[198]

It became 'them and us' all over again, only instead of war-bonds it was Warhol, instead of Nazis it was Knebworth. Doffing your hat? Eating with your mouth shut?? Giving your seat up to a pregnant woman on the Tube??? Today, you're more likely to be mugged for your hat, told to keep your mouth shut, and become pregnant on the Tube.

The Old Way still suffers its attacks, and I think society's the poorer for it, for not rescuing the best bits our forebears wanted to leave us. Integrity, Courtesy, Refinement and Culture do throw some folk into a muck sweat - those, for instance, on the front benches at Westminster. Yet all such scandals really do is remind of the old truism that your sins will find you out, even though you're not supposed to call them sins anymore. To me, the fact that scandals still abound shows the Old Morality is not defunct and still out there, sipping port in a gentlemen's club somewhere, perhaps still mulling over where it all went so tragically wrong.

---

[198] Hitchens, Peter, *The Abolition of Britain*, Quartet Books, 1999

'My Lord might consider *High Society* in the 3:45 at Aintree?'

'Damn me, Benson! Pass the Form!'

See also:
You're Never Too Old to Change
Think Good Thoughts, Don't Dwell on Evil
Listen to What Comes Out of Your Mouth
Don't Lose Your Joy
Work at Self-Improvement
Manage Your Anger
Own a Good Conscience
Start Complaining
Take Responsibility for Your Actions
Help Others
Have a Point to it All

~ 11 ~

Contact Someone Who Thinks You've Forgotten Them

Ships that pass in the night. They enter through one door and out through another, the thousands you meet in your life. A few made an impression, most probably didn't. I've caught up with old acquaintances and projects have spun off, ideas formed, destiny shaped. I owe more than a little thanks to those who have mentored me over the years: my parents, Ken Chare, John Phillips, Wendy Wallace, Jamie Johnson, William Meade-King.

Did you ever think about those whose lives you inspired?

And could go on inspiring?

See also:
Be Reliable
Think Good Thoughts, Don't Dwell on Evil
Work at Self-Improvement
Own a Good Conscience
Help Others
Have a Point to it All

~ 10 ~
Guard Your Dental Health

Dentist Bill Kellner-Read writes:

'Realistically, overall dental health in many societies today is not better than it was two decades ago. In fact, it's worse. And this is not necessarily because of the dentist's inability to fix the problems. We have at our disposal fantastic, state-of-the-art equipment and procedures to solve even the most complex of cases. The bottom-line is two-fold: the public hasn't learned to give up abusing their bodies with food, and the dentist hasn't learned to give up inflicting abuse on his patients caused by some of his treatments. There simply are no realistic, consistent efforts being made by dental medicine to prevent dental problems from occurring in our society in the first place.'[199]

Bill Read is, of course, referring to the lack of serious effort being made with the public's education on dietary habits, much less the dentist's. His book, *Toxic Bite*, is the first work I have read from a dental professional covering the real issues affecting the public with refreshing honesty:

'I discovered that many treatments available from a standard dental clinic today are based on entrenched scientific error,' he writes, *'as well as a fundamental, erroneous assumption of what caused the dental problem to begin with. I also uncovered surprising evidence that some of the most basic tenets*

[199] **Kellner-Read, Bill** *Toxic Bite,* Credence 2003

underpinning dentistry are flawed - and, even worse, downright dangerous.

Could it be that mercury amalgams, root canals, fluoride pastes, and others were benefiting the chemical industry more than the patient? And what of the burgeoning profits made from dentistry? Was there a connection between the levels of rotten teeth, gingivitis and bad breath consistently showing up in the neighbourhood, and the amount of paper whirring through the dental office credit-card machine? Was this a simple but unsettling case of sickness meaning big business?'[200]

On the Health Side:

- Could gum disease be responsible for heart disease and stroke?
- What products are we using every day that contribute to wider toxic illness?
- And what about extraction? Do we really need that tooth pulled?
- Should we be extracting children's teeth for orthodontic correction?
- What are the longer-term consequences of having less teeth in the mouth?
- Is there a link between nutrition and gum disease?

Bill Read reports cutting down on the obvious, such as bread, refined carbohydrates, cakes and candy, will make a serious dent in the acid and sugar that drives dental decay. Smoking, alcohol abuse, gum-chewing and other bagatelles are also perennial killers

---

[200] Kellner-Read, Bill *Toxic Bite,* Credence 2002 (Available from www.credence.org)

of gnashers. Soft drinks, sodas, sports drinks, sugar water and everything we drink on a hot day except *real water* should be avoided, not least due to the problems caused to the immune system.

Checklist

- **Choose a 'bio-friendly' dentist**
- **Have a great diet** – Eat organically grown, pesticide-free, living whole-foods, a high percentage eaten raw
- **Use nutritional supplements** - choose a company whose expertise is well known, whose products have a track record of efficacy (I recommend Neways). Baseline nutrition should include a highly bio-available vitamin and mineral supplement. Some also come with rare earths, amino acids, enzymes and other co-factors. An antioxidant supplement and daily Vitamin C I also recommend (see *The ABC's of Disease,* 'A Guide to Nutritional Supplements'). Don't overdo the supplements!
- **Good oral hygiene** – Brush properly and regularly after meals, floss and use a safe, effective mouthwash.
- **Safe products** – Use toothpastes and mouthwashes without sodium fluoride, and exchange your other personal care products, such as shampoo, conditioner, make-up, deodorants, etc. for safe alternatives (Neways also)
- **Eradication of toxins** – Rid your food, water and environment of known toxins
- **Safety for children** – Ensure a safe, nutritious environment for your children and train them up in health habits that will last a lifetime
- **Drink plenty of clean, pure water** (at least 2 litres/4 pints a day)

See also:

You're Never Too Old to Change
Set Goals Daily
You Are What You Eat
Get in the Raw
Choose the Right Doctor
Limit Caffeine, Alcohol and Carbonated Drinks
Supplement Real Vitamin C
Drink Two Litres of Water a Day
Remove Toxins from Home and Work
Juice Veggies
Exercise Prevention
There is Danger in Excess, Moderation in All Things
Avoid Sugar/Fat-Free Foods

Books available from www.credence.org:

Toxic Bite

~ 9 ~
Take Responsibility For Your Actions

'The reason there is so little crime in Germany is that it's against the law.' - **Alex Levin**

Here's a timely one in view of today's 'victim' culture, where no-one can slip on a banana skin without suing for a pay-out. We knew the compensation culture would catch up with us one day and it has. What really depresses me is the sheer number of sluggards crawling out of the woodwork to sticky their fingers with the hand-outs.

A police officer wants compensation because he's suffering 'post traumatic stress disorder' for attending car accidents. Here's my advice, mate. If you don't like blood, which, since you were not told, sadly goes with a policeman's duties, *get another job.* It should be that simple to understand, but clearly it's not. Why? Because you know you can get away with it. Because, if you bleat 'victim' loud enough, an ever-expanding army of shiny-reared, tax-gobbling jobsworths will fall over themselves to cough up your shame-money. And shame's what I call it when a society sticks two fingers up at moral rectitude and sees 'human rights' as nothing more than a fast-track payout to an indolent life.

Eight-year-old Cait Atkins is struck crossing a road in Aylesbury, UK and the driver does a runner - no surprises there. What happened next, or rather didn't, is the real shame. Up to a dozen cars drive around Cait's crumpled form as she lies in agony in the middle of the road. Not one stops to offer her assistance. One driver even waits impatiently for her to crawl out of the way.

Another scumbag, Barry Chambers, takes refuge on a Gloucester roof after allegedly stealing a car. He bombards the police with bricks and missiles. So, instead of going up there to fetch him down like we pay them to, Gloucester Plod buys the wretch a KFC meal, a bottle of Pepsi (the can was rejected in favour of a two-litre bottle) and a pack of fags so his rights aren't 'infringed'. In the unlikely event the plan was to plug up the fellow's arteries so he rolled off the roof and landed between the paws of a K9 unit, one could at least admire such *sui generis* creativity. Sadly, this wasn't the case.

A society no longer willing to teach right from wrong lets murderers out in five years, teaches three-year-old children 'gay diversity' to root out homophobes, and allows liars and criminals to serve in public office. Welcome to the hoodie culture. In fact, hug a hoodie today, as David Cameron urges, because it's not their fault they do what they do, it's yours for not liking Pee-Diddy in the first place.

A society is a reflection of the individuals who comprise it, and look what we've become. Was a time we fell off our bike, picked ourselves up, dusted ourselves off and carried on as if nothing had happened. Today, when we fall off our bike, we're dusted off by a social worker, referred into a victim support group, and if that doesn't work we can sue the government on legal aid. Alternatively, if we're slam-dunked by some appalling stroke of 'fate' such as wanton debt, an illicit affair or a Prozac or Valium dependency, we can slip into the 'victim' jacket and seek out the nearest agony aunt, astrologer or Feng Shui advisor. These are only too happy to oblige with the latest scoop, pocketing our money and reassuring us it's nothing *we* did, it's just society's a dog, the new moon's in the 11th house and the furniture's all in the wrong place.

To me, taking responsibility for your actions is a lot more than owning up to nicking a Wonderbra, it's a downright duty of care to get busy whenever a governing system starts losing the plot. As with all extremism, the later you confront it, the uglier the options become, and that goes for your own behaviour as well. Yet thousands abandon Britain each year, taking with them not just the Ambre-Solaire. They quit their jobs, sell up and leave the country because 'Britain was the problem', they didn't like it, didn't want to do anything about it, and, to paraphrase Voltaire, 'never having been able to succeed in the world, they took their revenge by speaking ill of it'. They got chased out of town.

What happened to 'the buck stops here'?

- There's nothing wrong with emigrating, just make sure *you're* not the problem
- Take responsibility for your actions
- Don't lie, cheat or steal!
- The grass is rarely greener. As George Moore says, *'A man travels the world over in search of what he needs, and returns home to find it'*
- If you don't like the way things are, take action and **Start Complaining**. From now on, let's have Outraged from Tunbridge Wells, Fed-Up from Fargo and Ticked Off from Toowoomba
- Be an upstanding citizen and campaign for the society you want
- **Own a Good Conscience**
- Be blameless
- Stand by your values and don't *ever* back down. Or, like the city of Gloucester, you'll soon discover allowing the loonies

free run of the asylum ends up costing rather more than just Barry's Bargain Bucket and a packet of Winstons.

~ 8 ~
'Be Disciplined

It is easier for a camel to pass through the eye of a needle if it is lightly greased

Discipline is setting your life to some sort of order, choosing goals and sticking to them, planning your future. What true discipline *shouldn't be* is an hour of pain with Madam Bow-Wow, extreme, robotic, unfeeling or Herr Flick in *'Allo Allo'*.

Discipline is the carburettor of your engine. You can be hectically tuned chaos or you can manage yourself smoothly even at high RPM. True discipline is *protective* not *punitive*. True discipline gives you your life back. To achieve something of worth you need discipline. To win you need discipline. To be happy you need discipline.

Bad Lads' Army is extreme discipline for extreme disciples. It's because humans crave structure that we've organised ourselves into nations, governments, councils, parties, football teams, committees, groups and gangs, which all run on discipline/law/code (same thing). When structure is denied the youth of today under bleeding-heart liberal policies promoting 'do what thou wilt' Crowlianism, the result is bad lads, dropped trousers on a Friday night and contempt and alienation of society. I read somewhere more people suffer alienation 'mental illnesses' today than ever before, which doesn't surprise me, a) because they make up these diseases and b) twenty years of 'we don't need no edjacayshun' has predictably resulted in the thick, self-obsessed trogs featured nightly on Big Brother.

Be Disciplined is about keeping the leash taut on a daily basis, but not overly so - just so stuff gets done. The strength of discipline required is commensurate with the extent of your goals. Don't put yourself under too much pressure over the long-term. Don't flog a dead horse. Navigate the middle course. Be an example, not a pain in the *derrière*.

See also:
You're Never Too Old to Change
Set Goals Daily
Be an Overcomer
Live in the Present
Simplify, Simplify, Simplify
There is Danger in Excess, Moderation in All Things
Be Reliable
Strive For Excellence
Listen to What Comes Out of Your Mouth
Don't Lose Your Joy
Work at Self-Improvement
Reward Yourself
Own a Good Conscience
Don't Break the Law
Experience Success
Take Responsibility for Your Actions
Be Thankful
Help Others
Have a Point to it All

- 7 -
Read a Good Book

Escapism comes in many forms, but one of the most cost-effective and enjoyable break-outs is a good book. I was never frightened the internet or computers would ring the death-knell for the printed word. As an author myself, I always print my work on paper. I've shunned e-books and other gimmicks and in my den at home have the most wonderful research library with a separate section for fiction.

Reading a good book is a break and relaxation, which experience has the capacity to change lives, tickle funny bones and inspire beyond measure. Good fiction especially enthrals, since you're inside the heads of the characters and observe the action in far greater detail than the most extravagantly filmed blockbuster. Imagination, imprisoned for decades in the Bastille of gossip mags and newspapers, can really run riot when you give it a good yarn to storm into.

As I write this, my eye roves over priceless rows of endeavour and fun: From Ballard's *The Military Genius of Abraham Lincoln* to *The Little Book of Toilet Graffiti*, from Magnus Magnusson's *Vikings* to Noel Botham's *The Ultimate Book of Useless Information,* get your own world together and be critical. Books that don't hold your attention are the author's fault. Don't overdose on fiction, which holds *conflict* as its central premise! Ever thought of writing a book of your own?

~ 6 ~
Give to Charities That Do the Job

Charities are good things. However, as with all human endeavours where there's a gob of money around, the flies can soon gather around the honey-pot, the unscrupulous operators move in, and the good intentions and gullibility of the public shamelessly exploited.

Just the mention of 'charity' carries respectability, has good folk delving into their pockets to cough up for that old duffer with his tin for leukaemia. Is he an unscrupulous operator? Hardly. But the industry persuading him to spend his valuable time outside Burger King can be.

I have covered research into the charity industry in some of my books - especially medical charities, or, as I term them, fund-raising institutions for the drug industry. The idea of soliciting contributions to fund research to consign cancer, arthritis, etc. to the history books is a laudable one, but only if that charity is prepared to fund nutrition research also that doesn't have a big drug pay-cheque at the end of it. That great bastion of health freedom, Professor Samuel Epstein, is renowned for hooking his talons into The American Cancer Society, the world's largest cancer charity which, he tells us, also makes political contributions.

'ACS... trivializes the escalating incidence of cancer which has reached epidemic proportions and makes grossly misleading claims on dramatic progress in the treatment and cure of cancer. This myopic mindset and derelict policy is compounded by interlocking

conflicts of interests with the cancer drug, agrichemical, and other industries.'[201]

Most money you give to cancer charities goes to fund research into a drug cure for cancer, and there can be no drug cure for cancer, any more than one for heart disease, arthritis, diabetes, psoriasis, scurvy and beri-beri, since these are metabolic issues that only have their resolutions in diet and lifestyle changes.[202] The one cancer charity I do endorse is the World Cancer Research Fund, which uses its cash to educate folks into not getting cancer in the first place.[203] They advocate this approach vehemently and are therefore awarded my Pink Elephant.

Of course, you're free to give money to who you want, who am I to tell you? But make your generosity count. Personally, I'd think twice before giving another penny to Live Aid, Live 8, Africa, 'AIDS', or other 'essential causes' until a) African leaders stop opening numbered Zurich accounts and b) I get some real proof, other than glossy documentaries, to convince me the money's doing what it should.

If you feel that strongly about a cause, why not start your own charity? I've known doctors set up nutrition clinics funded by donations. Great. I don't give to hospices unless they do something for patients other than sluicing them with drugs, doughnuts and milkshakes to help them 'die with dignity'. I do like WaterAid, whose charity-funded projects to date have enabled over 5 million

---

[201] Press release from the Cancer Prevention Coalition, Chicago, 25th October 1999, PRNewswire (see www.preventcancer.com)

[202] **Day, Phillip** *B17 Metabolic Therapy,* op. cit.

[203] www.wcrf.org

people around the world to gain access to safe water.[204] I like local projects I can keep my eye on. I like the Kent Air Ambulance, based in my home village, whizzing over my head. I was once first on the scene after a lady fell off her scooter, broke her shoulder and received serious head injuries from the blow to her helmet. That bloody chopper went from Marden to the Isle of Sheppey in 15 minutes flat and the lady eventually recovered. Brilliant.[205]

---

204 **WaterAid,** Freepost (SW1644), Prince Consort House, 27-29 Albert Embankment, LONDON SE1 7YY, Tel: +44(0)20 7793 4526

205 www.kentairambulance.co.uk

~ 5 ~
Forget the Lottery

And this one's in the same vein, since most lotteries see themselves as 'charities', with the added angle, of course, of your sad interest in the outcome.

- Do you play the lottery with any serious hope you can change your financial circumstances? If you do, then it's my duty to tell you you've as much chance of winning the lottery as Wiley Coyote has of becoming US president
- *Wait, Wiley Coyote is US president?*
- A flutter now and then is not what we're talking about. Hundreds of pounds' worth of tickets, scratch cards and assorted cack every month is what we're talking about
- And what's this 'Oh, I never play the Lotto until the jackpot's at least 20 million'? Like 5 million wouldn't fit square in your wedge if the pigs came back to Earth?
- And those worthy causes the money goes to, what of the National Lottery's track-record to date? *The IRA? Programs designed to prevent the deportation of illegal aliens?? A scheme to fatten guinea-pigs for Peruvians to eat???*
- If you're that strapped for cash, I'll send you a fiver
- Better still, why not design a serious game-plan to get yourself out of financial meltdown, or if your angle's the charity end, see previous chapter or set up your own. At least you'll know where the money's going.

See also:
Moderation in All Things, There's Danger in Excess
Attack Political Correctness

~ 4 ~

Be Thankful

'The two-foot long New Zealand mountain bird kea likes to eat the strips of rubber around car windows.'

- The Ultimate Book of Useless Information

There have been times I've been poor and times I've been OK. Take it from me, OK's far better and for that I'm thankful, but not for the obvious reasons. It's nice to have some spare cash lying around, but even nicer not to have to worry about where the next meal's coming from. Most of the behavioural experts, such as Chopra, Robbins and Tracy, spend some time getting their students out of the 'poverty mentality', and I've side-swiped this issue in a number of chapters relating to goal-setting and changing attitudes, not least about money.

Napoleon Hill's *Think and Grow Rich* became a classic years ago because it got the reader to change their mindset and start viewing their substance from a totally different viewpoint, not greed but the desire for *abundance.*

- You're no more or less worthy of success than Bill Gates or Richard Branson
- What determines your success is your strategy
- Be consistent
- Don't take no for an answer
- Be moral
- Be thankful

You could fill your own library with all the self-help tomes, get-rich-quick tapes and 'Plan Your Sparkling Future' DVD's on the market, but I think one of the most fundamental issues is what you give life *consistently* and what life gives you in return. The Principle of Reciprocity is sensed by almost everyone and is variously referred to as *karma, 'Do unto others as you would have them do unto you', 'You reap what you sow', 'As a man thinks in his heart, so is he'.* There seems to exist also a principle of thanking the universe for what you have (even if it isn't much) and getting more doors opened in return. Strange but true.

Consider that scientist Cleve Backster got plants to react to him by hooking them up to a lie-detector (Backster invented them). Apparently, like humans and animals, other carbon-based life-forms react better to upbeat, optimistic feelings and get downright suicidal when you curse them. What if the universe is set up that way too?

Backster finished some complicated experiments with an uncomplicated conclusion: Life is most content when it's in harmony with its surroundings. Obvious, yet stunning. Like love and music, being thankful buys into a primal phenomenon we don't understand yet, that there's always something to be thankful for, and always someone to thank, and for that more doors are opened, and that seems to be the way of it until you stop believing and being thankful, and then they call it bi-polar.

I think being thankful:

- Re-aligns your ego
- Corrects pride
- Reaffirms your relationship to the world and others
- Humanizes you

- Subordinates you to the Higher Power, whatever you perceive that to be

Think about it. You've got food on the table, clothes on your back and a few quid in the bank, which is more than most people on this planet have. And if you have your health also, you're basically in the top 1%.

So be thankful.

Stop complaining for a minute!

~ 3 ~

Enjoy Music

'A violin is the revenge exacted by the intestines of a dead cat.' - **Ambrose Bierce**

Music is a primal force like love and reciprocity. We don't know how it affects us, only that it does. In **Enjoy Silence,** I cover the times when silence is golden, indeed necessary. Other times, by all means let your hair down and enjoy the sound of life. Enjoy music.

The best that's known so far is that plants enjoy music. Human patients heal and exercise better in the presence of certain types of music[206] (except Ozzy Ozbourne). Dr Joseph Mercola writes:

'Dr Masaru Emoto from Japan began studying the impact of altering water by various factors of vibration and consciousness. He studied water that had been altered by music - healing music, classical music, heavy metal music.'[207]

Emoto's work caused quite a stir because it seems to reveal that water is alive and responds to applied force *'by a rearrangement of its inner crystalline properties.'*[208] Considering the human body is majority water, Dr Emoto says we should actually care what sounds, words and vibrations we expose ourselves to. Sound familiar?

---

[206] EurekAlert!, 23rd March 2004, www.eurekalert.org

[207] www.mercola.com

[208] Ibid. See **Emoto M and David Thayne** *The Hidden Messages in Water,* Beyond Words Publishing, 2004 (available through Amazon)

Well, there's music and music. Beethoven to Band-Aid, Chopin to Sheryl Crow. Depending on the genre, music has been found to:

- Help ward off senile dementia and Alzheimer's [209]
- Help heal
- Relax
- Relieve depression
- Ease pain
- Provoke extreme aggression in teens [210]
- Cause hearing damage

An interesting study on the (anti)social effects of modern music is covered in my *Mind Game* chapter, 'Gunning for the Young'. Because of Pavlov's Principle, repetition of violent, abrasive music can have some rather debilitating effects on the listener, and this coming from no prude in matters music. You'll be pleased to hear I don't believe all pop/rock songs are demonic, and no-one would seriously pretend so, but those preaching anti-social messages to their millions of slavish acolytes were certainly getting *Focus on the Family* all up in a tiswas, and that *did* interest me.

Years later, I applied myself to an in-depth study of the effects of music and was fascinated to uncover consistent patterns running through the counter-culture. The most notable of which were reported, unsettling encounters with what seemed at first sight to be the Dark Lord himself.

---

[209] Proceedings of the National Academy of Sciences, 13th March 2001, 98:3440

[210] Journal of the American Academy of Child and Adolescent Psychiatry, April 2001, 40:392-401.

While recording his hit *Great Balls of Fire*, Jerry Lee Lewis repeatedly told his producer he was demon-possessed.[211] Little Richard stated: *'I was directed and commanded by another power. The power of darkness. The power you've heard so much about. The power people believe doesn't exist. The power of the devil. We must realise that there is a force that is fighting against us in this world... the devil was controlling our minds, directing our lives.'*[212]

According to his own writings, Jim Morrison of the Doors used psychiatric drug-induced altered states to make contact with the demonic realm. Morrison was having a hard time at UCLA in the '60's and dropped out of film school to live in Venice, California. He writes:

"In that year there was an intense visitation of energy. I left school and went down to the beach to live. I slept on a roof. At night the moon became a woman's face. I met the Spirit of Music.... an appearance of the devil on a Venice canal. Running, I saw a Satan, or Satyr, moving beside me, a fleshly shadow of my secret mind. Running. Knowing."[213]

Morrison later identified this Spirit, or Angel of Music, as Satan. He went on to state that it was through such demonic tutorship that he received many of the ideas for his hit songs, remarking of these drug experiences, *'It was like being at a fantastic rock concert, I just took notes.'*[214] Morrison would later

---

[211] Herman, Gary, *Rock and Roll Babylon*, Plexus Publishing, 2002

[212] Schimmel, Joe, *Rock and Roll Sorcerers of the New Age Revolution,* a video presentation, Fight the Good Fight, Simi Valley, CA: 1993.

[213] Ibid.

[214] Ibid.

admit he was 'led' to write songs with lyrics such as *"Cancel my subscription to the Resurrection. Send my credentials to the House of Detention, I've got some friends inside."* And, *"Music is your special friend. Dance on fire as it intends. Music is your only friend, until the end."*

Well, legend does hold Lucifer himself was once the Angel of Music who led the worship of God, and I'm sure the mushrooms and mescalin wouldn't have helped either, but was this hyperbole and posturing by the stars mere hubris, or were many experiencing problems they had no clue how to confront?

'Spirits' caused Brian Wilson of the Beach Boys such torment that on one occasion, he was bedridden for four years because of the paranoia and mental angst that came upon him. LSD is known to cause symptoms attributed to demon possession and the classic psychiatric definition of 'schizophrenia'. Immense success and musical prestige came to The Beach Boys apparently with a high penalty in suffering. *Rolling Stone* magazine, 11th August 1988, records:

'Brian Wilson hears voices. They talk to him, they distract him, frighten him, confuse him. Right now, as the genius behind the California surf-rock sound sits in his darkened living room, the Pacific crashing loudly outside his million-dollar Malibu home, the voices are calling. The 46-year-old screws up his face and his eyes roll towards the ceiling -'

Brian Wilson also experienced the automatic writing/contact phenomenon described by Jim Morrison and could not play the music he recorded. Before embarking on tour, this musical genius had to relearn all his chords and lyrics.

One of the more controversial bands of the 1990's was Jane's Addiction. Lead singer Perry Farrell set out to overturn every moral convention, exposing and fondling himself on stage and on occasion performing naked throughout an entire concert. Raised in New York the son of a jeweller and an artist mother who committed suicide when Farrell was four, the young rebel moved to Los Angeles and worked as an exotic dancer posing as various rock stars. He remarks:

'I say you don't have anything - you don't have a society, unless that society is completely shameless. If you're shameless, you feel like your impulses, as long as they're within both people's free will, those impulses are fine.'[215]

And, predictably:

When I want something and I don't want to pay for it
Then I walk right through the door
Yeah I walk right through the door
Hey all right
If I get by
It's mine.
(Jane's Addiction, *Been Caught Stealing*, Warner Bros.)

Mr Farrell isn't the only one trying to get out from under the rug of accountability:

'Imagine Alice Cooper times 10. Picture KISS on an acid and whiskey bender. Marry the gross-out hilarity of G G Allin with the ubiquity of Howard Stern. Combine the 'search and destroy'

---

[215] *Spin Magazine* June 1991, p.80

frenzy of Iggy Pop with the godless zeal of Ozzy Osbourne. Take two cups of the devil and throw in a pinch of P T Barnum, and you still can't fathom all that is... Marilyn Manson.

Spawning a cult following to rival all others, Manson and his rotating band of serial-killer sidemen have created a powerful concoction of Satanic imagery, face-splitting guitars and performance spectacle that has drawn the ire of countless keepers of the public good.'[216]

Notwithstanding the appeal of rock, pop and rap lies in its iconoclastic rebellion (and yes, I did wind my Led Zeppelin LPs backwards with spectacular results), societies must have moral order so they can function. History demonstrates that when the family unit is disrupted, when society unhooks itself from the last constraints of a collective moral code, then it's all down the gurgler from there. Is it plain to see when the concepts of right and wrong are blurred, people believe they are free to do what is right in their own eyes? Do crime and lawlessness increase as a result? Are lives wrecked? Are the stars themselves happier living the reported 'truths' of their lifestyles? The truth, I suspect, lies somewhere between the two extremes, and so must we.

In conclusion, music's great, man, but be aware of the power.

See also:
Be Inspired
Guard Input

---

[216] www.rollingstone.com

~ 2 ~
Help Others

'Help a man in trouble and he'll never forget you - especially the next time he's in trouble.' - **Johnny Lyons**

Helping others distinguishes a civilised society from a barbaric one. There are two kinds of needy people:

- Those who can't help themselves
- And those who can

Teaching others to help themselves is by far the most successful strategy - most problems in the First World are those we can do something about, such as sickness, poverty, ignorance, violence and crime. But do we have the political will? Teaching our children the life skills required to overcome should be a top priority for our schools but sadly isn't. More and more, citizens are coming to rely on the state, which is only too happy to oblige. More committees are formed, taxes go up and you know the rest. Big Brother taking care of everything, only he never does, so neither do we.

Personal initiative, motivation, charity and passion cannot help but give birth to a lean and healthy civilisation. These are worthy goals but we have to want them. Perhaps only by living the worst of the two extremes first will we eventually choose the middle course. Sadly the harshest lessons are those learnt through pain.

Helping others is teaching them to overcome. It's owning a good conscience. It's thinking good thoughts and not dwelling on evil. It's knowing about weed-killer in the garden section of a DIY store, for goodness sake, *if that's supposed to be your job.* Gad, now we have ironmongers who know nothing about ironmongery, supermarket assistants who can't string two words together, mechanics who don't, plumbers who won't, and hotels that can't feed you past midnight *because we're not really a hotel, Sir, we're an 'express' hotel, so I sit here and do nothing, that being the meaning of the word 'express', Sir.*

Translated: *Express yourself out of here, Sir.*

Not so in America. You phone reception at 2am, and after half a ring, here's what you get: *'Good morning, Room Service, my name is Greg. How may I assist the Day party of two?'* Now that's impressive. I like assistance from Americans, even when they cock up. We're born naked and screaming into this world and then it gets worse, so I'm here to help you, and you help me, and that's the way it's supposed to work, right?

That means knowing what's wrong with my car after you just charged me £245 plus VAT and gave me the bits to take home in a Jiffy bag. It means don't burst into my hotel-room like the Charge of the Light Brigade if there's a sign outside that reads, *Sshh! We're Sleeping!* Care enough to do your job. It's not cool to be dumb. When you're rubbish, it's just rubbish. You are in control of your destiny. *Make good choices.* As covered in this and my other books, take simple steps to amend diet, lifestyle and attitude and witness superb results. In fact,

- Use this book as a stocking-filler
- If anyone objects, blame Santa
- Help others!

~ 1 ~
Have A Point to It All

'He was a great patriot, a humanitarian, a loyal friend - provided, of course, he is really dead.' - **Voltaire**

And finally, we've taken such trouble to live life this far, what makes us continue? Why strive at all? We're born, we live, we die - can you sign off on a life?

As I write, I am sitting in a hotel room somewhere in England, shoes off, hands behind head, and snap back to the present. The pictures on the walls have been faded blue by our Riviera sun. They all feature bloomer-clad beauties frolicking in the surf from a long-dead era when a dog could be called Nigger, a gay caballero was a jocular Spaniard, and bitching made pups. The windows around me will only open a few inches in case I try to commit suicide. The bathroom fan sounds like the Luftwaffe's back. There's no food after nine.

The free hotel magazine tells me *Sex Burns 370 Calories, Enough for One Ginger Biscuit at Any Rate*. Life's good, I decide, and I'm thankful for it, though this year I'm 46 and there's hair growing out of my ears, so all the cares in the world, then, and I'm turning into a bloody rabbit. I'm glad I no longer have to go to school. I like the feeling when I come off the treadmill at the gym and glide across the floor like a Dalek. And yes, there will always be those less fortunate than I am so I will do my best for them, for that is my mission.

Somewhere a woman is putting herself to bed, wishing her husband still looked at her the way he looks at his Kentucky Fried

Chicken. Garry Glitter may go before a firing squad for molesting girls in Cambodia (talk about two worlds colliding). Every ten seconds, somewhere in the world, a woman gives birth to a child. I think we should find this person and stop her immediately.

There are three Indian restaurants in my village now and I'm thinking, what do they know that I don't? I still hate hotels and concede that sometimes happiness can be a belt-fed weapon. I even wonder what this dream was all about. What difference did I make? How will I be remembered? What qualities did I possess? Was I worth it?

Life, then, a question of choices. The high or the low road? The porn or the promise? Desire over temperance? Food or illusions? *Who's taking notes?*

Does the noise in my head *bother you?*

THE END

The *Food For Thought* Dietary Regimen

Try this!

- Little or no meat in the diet. Any meat consumed should be hormone and pesticide-free. White meat is better than red. Avoid pork
- Avoid sugar, dairy, coffee and alcohol
- Eat properly constituted, organic, whole, living foods, a high percentage raw. If you want hot, briefly steam your veggies. Do not murder them. Remember that heat kills enzymes. Excellent recipes are provided in our companion guide, *Food For Thought*
- The ideal balance is: 80% alkali/20% acidic ash foods. Most diets today comprise 90% acid/10% alkali!
- Some broiled fish, deep and cold caught, eaten sparingly is OK
- Avoid the foods below
- Hydrate the body (2 litres (4 pints) of clean, fresh water a day)
- Keep high-glycaemic fruit intake down. Eat more fruits that have low sugar-conversion, such as pears and apples
- Juice veggies
- Eat six *small* meals a day, ensuring a) that you don't go hungry, and b) that the body has a constant supply of nutrients
- **THE BASIC SUPPLEMENT PROGRAM** will consist of ionised colloidal trace minerals, antioxidant tablets, Vit C and B complexes and essential fats
- Exercise (to get everything moving and assist in detoxing the body in an oxygen-rich environment). A regular walk in the early morning air is also healthy and very invigorating
- Rest. Rest. Rest. Rest. Rest

- Reduce environmental toxicity (avoid jobs using dangerous chemicals, radiation, etc.)
- Use safe personal care products (Neways)
- Use safe household products (Neways)

Foods to Avoid

- Pork products (bacon, sausage, hot-dogs, luncheon meat, ham, etc.) These are high in nitrites and are known homotoxins which can cause high blood urea and dikitopiprazines, which cause brain tumours and leukaemia.[217]
- Scavenger meats (inc. ALL shellfish and other carrion-eaters - see Leviticus 11 in the Bible). Carrion-eaters, pork and shellfish in particular, concentrate toxins of other animals in their tissues, which we then consume to our detriment. The same goes for the elimination organs of commercially raised animals, such as liver and kidney, which can be high in drug and pesticide residues
- Aspartame/saccharin, artificial sweeteners. These are known mental impairment problems and cancer risks.
- Refined sugar/flour/rice. SUCROSE FEEDS CANCER Restricted amounts of wholegrain bread are OK. Use only wholegrain rice. No sugars should be consumed other than those contained naturally in whole foods
- Hydrogenated & partially hydrogenated fats (margarine)
- Junk (processed) food, including fizzy sodas and other soft drinks containing sugar, artificial sweeteners or phosphoric acid, which are drunk out of aluminium cans
- Fat-free foods. Essential fats are *essential*!

---

[217] Day, Phillip, *Food for Thought*, op. cit; *Biologic Therapy*, "Adverse influence of pork consumption on human health", Vol. 1, No. 2, 1983

- Olestra, canola, soy, etc. Avoid fake or synthetic fats. Soy, in its unfermented state (meat and milk substitute products), disrupts the hormone (endocrine) system, blocks the absorption of calcium and magnesium, and acts like estrogen in the body. Small usage of fermented soy products is OK (soy sauce, miso, etc). For more information on soy, see **The Shadow of Soy** in *The ABC's of Disease*, *Food For Thought*, or *Health Wars*
- Polluted water (chlorinated or fluoridated - see *Health Wars*, **Water Under the Bridge**)
- Caffeine products
- Alcohol products
- Excess refined salt. Use Himalayan salt instead.

For a full analysis of 'food as it should be', see *Food For Thought*, the food recipe companion to *Simple Changes*

Common Alkali Ash Foods

(help to control acid in your internal environment)[218]

Almonds
Apples
Apricots
Avocados
Bananas
Beans, dried
Beet greens
Beet
Blackberries
Broccoli
Brussels sprouts
Cabbage
Carrots
Cauliflower
Celery
Chard leaves
Cherries, sour
Cucumbers
Dates, dried
Figs, dried
Grapefruit
Grapes
Milk, goat*
Millet
Molasses
Mushrooms
Muskmelons
Onions
Oranges (small amounts)
Parsnips
Peaches
Pears
Pineapple
Potatoes, sweet
Potatoes, white
Radishes
Raisins
Raspberries
Rutabagas
Sauerkraut
Soy beans, green
Spinach, raw
Strawberries

* Recommended for infants only when mother's milk is not available.

Note: Some of the above foods may seem acidic but leave an alkali ash in the system. Bolded foods are B17 nitrilosides.

Convert your diet to 80% alkali ash/ 20% acid ash foods. Ensure that your diet is predominant high-water content foods that are fresh and organic.

[218] Morter, E T, op. cit.

Common Acid Ash Foods

Bacon
Barley grain
Beef
Blueberries
Bran, wheat
Bran, oat
Bread, white
Bread, whole wheat
Butter
Carob
Cheese
Chicken
Cod
Corn
Corned beef
Crackers, soda
Cranberries
Currants
Eggs
Flour, white
Flour, whole wheat
Haddock
Macaroni
Oatmeal
Oysters
Peanut butter
Peanuts
Peas, dried
Pike
Plums ^
Pork
Prunes ^
Rice, brown
Rice, white
Salmon
Sardines
Sausage
Scallops
Shrimp
Spaghetti
Squash, winter
Sunflower seeds
Turkey

^ These foods leave an alkaline ash but have an acidifying effect on the body.

NEUTRAL ASH FOODS THAT HAVE AN ACIDIFYING EFFECT

Corn oil   Corn syrup   Olive oil   Refined sugar

Foods Rich In Vitamin B17

- apple seeds
- alfalfa sprouts
- apricot kernels
- bamboo shoots
- barley
- beet tops
- bitter almond
- blackberry
- boysenberry
- brewer's yeast
- brown rice
- buckwheat
- cashews
- cassava (tapioca)
- cherry kernels
- cranberry
- eucalyptus leaves
- currants
- fava beans
- flax seeds
- garbanzo beans
- gooseberry
- green peas
- huckleberry
- kidney beans
- lentils
- lima beans
- linseed meat
- loganberries
- macadamia nuts
- millet
- millet seed
- mulberry
- nectarine kernels
- peach kernels
- pear seeds
- pecans
- plum kernels
- quince
- raspberry
- sorghum cane syrup
- spinach
- sprouts (alfalfa, lentil, mung bean, buckwheat, garbanzo)
- squash seeds
- strawberry
- walnuts
- watercress
- yams

Other Disorders

(where to go for more information)

THE ABC'S OF DISEASE is Credence's index compendium on over eighty disorders, what they are, what the symptoms are, and what can be done about them nutritionally, according to experts. For more information on specific disorders:

Chicken pox, opportunistic (infectious) diseases, influenza (flu), malaria, measles, mumps, rubella, severe acute respiratory syndrome (SARS), smallpox, tuberculosis, typhoid, etc.
See: ***Wake up to Health in the 21st Century***
by Steven Ransom

Cancers: brain, bowel, breast, cervical, liver, lung, osteo, ovarian, pancreatic, prostate, skin, etc.
See: ***Cancer: Why We're Still Dying to Know the Truth***
by Phillip Day
Also: ***Great News on Cancer in the 21st Century***
by Steven Ransom

Bad breath, constipation, diarrhoea, oesophageal reflux, heart diseases, high blood pressure, lactose intolerance, poisonings, putrefaction and misc. digestion problems
See: ***Health Wars***
by Phillip Day

ADD/ADHD, agitation, amnesia, anorexia nervosa, antisocial behaviour, autism, bedwetting, bulimia, chemical imbalances, convulsions, criminal behaviour, depression, drug addiction, dyslexia, epilepsy, facial swelling, glucose intolerance, hallucinations, hirsutism, histadelia, histapenia, hyperactivity, hypersexuality, infantile colic, irritability, leaky gut syndrome, nerve pain, nightmares, phobias, schizophrenia, seizures, smoking addiction, stress, suicidal tendencies, twitches

See: ***The Mind Game***
by Phillip Day

Acquired Immuno-Deficiency Syndrome and related disorders
See: The Truth About HIV
By Steven Ransom and Phillip Day

These titles and more are available through Credence's website at:

www.credence.org

Contacts! Contacts! Contacts!

If you wish to purchase more copies of this booklet or obtain any of Credence's other book and tape products, please use the contact details below. Credence has local sales offices in a number of countries. Please see our website at **www.credence.org** for further details:

UK Orders: (01622) 832386
UK Fax: (01622) 833314
www.credence.org
e-mail: sales@credence.org

Obtaining Health Products

If you need more information or help with any of the materials discussed in this book, please use the above contact details. Alternatively, you may contact:

Credence Publications
PO Box 3
TONBRIDGE
Kent TN12 9ZY
England
infopack@credence.org

The Campaign for Truth in Medicine

WHAT IS CTM?

The Campaign for Truth in Medicine is a worldwide organisation dedicated to educating the public on health issues and pressing for change in areas of science and medicine where entrenched scientific error, ignorance and vested interests are costing lives. Our ranks comprise doctors, scientists, researchers, bio-chemists, politicians, industry executives and members of the public, all of who have come to recognise that in key areas of disease, drug treatments and healthcare philosophy, the medical, chemical and political establishments are pursuing the wrong course with the maximum of precision, even when their own scientific research has warned of the dangers of these courses.

CTM STANDS FOR CHOICE IN HEALTHCARE

Millions today use nutritional supplements and alternative health strategies for themselves and their families, yet increasingly the public's freedom to choose is being eroded by government legislation and attempts by the pharmaceutical conglomerates to 'buy out' the alternative health market. CTM stands for the people's right to choose the healthcare system they feel is right for them, free of big business interference, pointless government regulation, and coercion by the medical establishment which often attempts to compel its own dubious remedies upon an unwilling public.

CTM STANDS FOR SPREADING THE GOOD NEWS

Every month, CTM sends out EClub, its global online magazine, to keep subscribers informed of the latest news, developments, scandals and great news in healthcare and other relevant issues. Within EClub, doctors, researchers, journalists, scientists and leading healthcare advocates share their tips, views and strategies with hundreds of thousands around the world. EClub represents the news you are not being told; information that can literally change and save lives. Don't miss out on this vital resource, forwarded FREE to you every month! To join, please visit campaignfortruth.com and click on the 'Join' tab.

Be part of a different future. One that celebrates life!

HOW TO ORDER CREDENCE PRODUCTS

Credence has offices and distributors in many countries around the world. If you would like more information, or wish to purchase any of the Credence titles described, please use the details in the **Contacts!** section of this book. Alternatively, why not visit Credence's comprehensive web-site at **www.credence.org**, which contains secure on-line global stores, a fully searchable database, our famous testimonies section, and many other great features.

Please note: Items not available in your regional shop may be obtained through our default 'Rest of World' store.

About the Author

Phillip Day was born in England in 1960. He was educated at Selwyn and Charterhouse, and throughout his twenties had a successful entrepreneurial career founding businesses in sales and marketing. With a firm grounding in the ways of the media, Phillip's research career began after he became interested in wars going on in the realms of health and politics over issues that were being deliberately withheld or misreported to the public.

Phillip Day heads up the publishing and research organisation Credence, now located in many countries around the world, which collates the work provided by researchers in many fields. Credence's intention is to work with the establishments and organisations concerned to resolve issues that are harming the public, and to provide the necessary information for citizens to make their own informed choices in these vital matters. Phillip's speaking schedule takes him to audiences all over the world.

Phillip Day is married to Samantha and lives in Kent, England.